ExplOring maths

Class Book

3

PEARSON
Longman

Series editor: **Anita Straker**

Published and distributed by Pearson Education Limited, Edinburgh Gate, Harlow, Essex, CM20 2JE, England
www.longman.co.uk

First published 2008
ISBN-13 978-1-405-84411-6

Freelance development editor: Sue Glover

Typeset by Tech-Set, Gateshead

Printed and bound in Great Britain at Scotprint, Haddington

The publisher's policy is to use paper manufactured from sustainable forests.

Picture Credits

The publisher would like to thank the following for their kind permission to reproduce their photographs:
(Key: b-bottom; c-centre; l-left; r-right; t-top)

Alamy Images: Adams Picture Library 235; Bubbles Photolibrary 141; David R. Frazier Photolibrary, Inc 145; David Young-Wolff 34; Directphoto.org 281; Golden Pixels LLC 68; Jeff Greenberg 40b, 138r, 303; Angela Hampton Picture Library 76; Mike Hill 143; Horizon International Images Limited 178b; Justin Leighton 82; Graham Oliver 232; PhotoAlto 53; Photofusion Picture Library 270t; Purestock 300; Redfx 273; Helene Rogers 81; RubberBall 244; Phil Talbot 167 (a); Libby Welch 177; Yadid Levy 117; **Art Directors and TRIP photo Library:** Helene Rogers 214; **Corbis:** Bettmann 90t, 200; Randy Faris 113t; Steve Raymer 31; **DK Images:** 54, 63b, 96l, 170, 183, 188, 227t, 257; Andy Crawford 226, 266tc; Dave King 32, 266tr; David Murray and Jules Selmes 108; Steve Gorton 92, 229, 264; Nelson Hancock © Rough Guides 191; Nigel Hicks 278; Jerry Young 182; Lindsey Stock 270bl, 270br; Max Alexander 180; Tim Ridley 47, 96r, 107r; Tim Ridley / Ted Taylor - modelmaker 61t; **Getty Images:** Adam Pretty/Allsport Concepts 288; Mike Powell/Allsport Concepts 63t, 301; Jess Stock/Stone 2; Tony Page /Stone 41; **iStockphoto:** 74t, 107c, 113b, 126, 208; Vera Bogaerts 103; Kelly Cline 206; Christina Clouston 97; Norma Cornes 178t; Adam Crawford 138l; Les Cunliffe 234; Simon Fenton 212r; Juan David Ferrando 115; Ieva Geneviciene 96c; Andrew Green 212l; David Gunn 272; Gerville Hall 20t; Karim Hesham 217; Inga Ivanova 255; Alexander Kataytsev 271; Birgitte Magnus 185; Alexandru Magurean 83l; Stuart Monk 114t; David Newton 243; Marcelo Piotti 167t; Toon Possemiers 132; Viktor Pravdica 40t; Stephen Rees 99; Amanda Rohde 266tl; Rick Sargeant 107l; Chris Schmidt 245; Jean Schweitzer 277; Oksana Struk 73b; Sami Suni 152; Robert Szajkowski 211; Seana van der Valk 167 (d); Vasiliki Varvaki 65; **Jupiter Unlimited:** 90b; AbleStock.com 83r; BananaStock 147; Brand X 283; Brand X Pictures 131; Comstock 142, 167 (b); Goodshoot 162; Liquidlibrary 167 (c); PhotoObjects.net 87, 227b; Thinkstock Images 73t, 83c; **PA Photos:** Michael Burke/AP 186; **Pearson Education Ltd:** 5, 74b, 120, 205; Pearson Learning 20b; PH College 114b, 129; Prentice Hall School Division 19, 44, 61b; Prentice Hall, Inc 274l; Prentice Hall, Inc. 274r; Scott Foresman 127; Silver Burdett Ginn 13, 15, 16, 21, 228; **PunchStock:** Stockbyte 59; **Rex Features:** SNAP 122; **Science Photo Library Ltd:** Francoise Sauze 249; **Frank Siteman:** 156

Cover images: Front: **Adam Periperl**

All other images © Pearson Education

Picture Research by: Louise Edgeworth

Every effort has been made to trace the copyright holders and we apologise in advance for any unintentional omissions. We would be pleased to insert the appropriate acknowledgement in any subsequent edition of this publication.

Contents

Properties of numbers

This unit will help you to:

- order, add and subtract positive and negative numbers;
- know the order for adding, subtracting, multiplying and dividing, and how to use brackets;
- find squares and square roots of whole numbers, including with a calculator;
- use tests to see what numbers will divide exactly;
- recognise multiples, factors and prime numbers up to 100.

1 Positive and negative integers

This lesson will help you to order, add and subtract positive and negative numbers.

Integers include positive and negative whole numbers and zero.

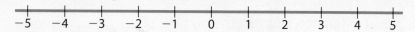

Numbers get less as you count back along the number line, so that -4 is less than -2. Look at these three signs: $<, =, >$.

$6 < 7$	$4 - 3 = 2 - 1$	$7 - 3 > 9 - 7$
6 is less than 7	**4 − 3 is equal to 2 − 1**	**7 − 3 is greater than 9 − 7**

To **add a positive number**, count on along the number line.
To **add a negative number**, count back along the number line.

Add 1 and -4.

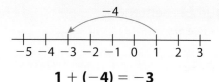

$$1 + (-4) = -3$$

Add -3 and 5.

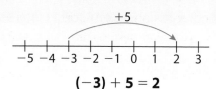

$$(-3) + 5 = 2$$

To **find a difference** between a pair of positive or negative numbers, find the change that takes you from the second number to the first.
If you count back, the answer is negative. If you count on, the answer is positive.

Find the difference between −4 and 1.

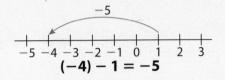

$(-4) - 1 = -5$

Find the difference between 2 and −4.

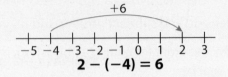

$2 - (-4) = 6$

Exercise 1

1. At dawn, the temperature was −2°C.
   By midday, the temperature was 5°C.
   By how much did the temperature rise?

2. The temperature in Paris was −2°C.
   At Chamonix, in France, it was −7°C.
   How much colder was it in Chamonix than in Paris?

3. Yesterday, the river was 10 cm below sea level.
   After some rain, it was 5 cm above sea level.
   How many centimetres did the water level rise?

4. To work out a goal difference, subtract the number of goals against from the number of goals for.

   Here are the goal differences of five football teams.
   Write the teams in order from the best to the worst goal difference.

Rovers	4
City	−3
Wanderers	5
United	−4
Rangers	−2

5. Work out these sums and differences.
   a $4 + (-2)$
   b $(-3) + 5$
   c $(-5) + (-4)$
   d $6 + (-7)$
   e $(-8) + 3$
   f $(-4) + 2 + (-3)$
   g $5 - (-2)$
   h $(-7) - 3$
   i $(-3) - (-10)$
   j $(-10) - (-3)$

6. Put the correct sign, $<$ or $=$ or $>$, into each number sentence.
   a $0 \ldots -3$
   b $-7 \ldots -2$
   c $3 - 2 \ldots -5$
   d $5 - 5 \ldots 4 - 6$
   e $-5 - 2 \ldots -3$
   f $-3 + 6 \ldots -1 + 4$
   g $(-2) + (-2) \ldots (-5) + 1$
   h $(-2) - (-3) \ldots (-1) + (-4)$

Did you know that...?

About 4000 years ago, China was ruled by the Emperor Fuh-hi. A story about him says that when he was sailing up the Yellow River he saw a turtle in the water. A strange sign was written on the turtle's back called a *lo-shu*. In the *lo-shu*, the sum of the numbers in any row, column or diagonal is always the same.

A square like this is called a **magic square**. Many people think it brings good luck.

the *lo-shu*

7   This is a magic square.
    Each row adds up to 3.
    Each column adds up to 3.
    Each diagonal adds up to 3.

    Copy the square.
    Fill in the missing numbers.

−2	...	...
3	1	...
2	...	4

8   As you go up the pyramid, each number is the sum of the two below it.

    Copy and complete these pyramids.

	21	
11		10

| 2 | 9 | 1 |

a
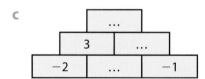

b
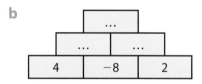

c

	...	
3		...
−2	...	−1

d
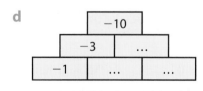

Points to remember

⊙ Numbers get smaller as you count back along the number line, so −8 < −4.

⊙ To add a positive number, count on along the number line.
   To add a negative number, count back along the number line.

⊙ Adding −6 is the same as subtracting 6.
   Subtracting −6 is the same as adding 6.

2 Order of operations and brackets

This lesson will help you to know the order for doing addition, subtraction, multiplication and division and how to do calculations with brackets.

There is an order for doing addition, subtraction, multiplication and division.
Multiply and divide before you add and subtract.

Example 1   Work out $5 + 6 \times 7$.

$5 + 6 \times 7 = 5 + 42 = 47$, because you work out 6×7 first.

If there are brackets, always work out expressions inside the brackets first.

Example 2   Work out $2 \times (3 + 4)$.

$2 \times (3 + 4) = 2 \times 7 = 14$, because you work out the brackets first.

Exercise 2

1 For each calculation, predict the result your calculator will give.
   Check with your calculator.

   a $8 \div 2 \times 5$ b $25 - 15 \div 3$ c $5 + 2 \times 3$ d $18 - 7 + 2$
   e $6 + 12 \div 4$ f $16 - 3 \times 5$ g $4 \times 10 \div 5$ h $9 + 5 \times 6$

2 **Without using a calculator**, work out:

   a $5 + 10 \times 5$ b $20 - 16 \div 4$ c $19 - 10 - 5$ d $5 \times 8 + 1$
   e $24 \div 2 + 6$ f $15 - 5 \times 2$ g $21 + 9 \div 3$ h $5 \times 9 \div 3$

3 **Without using a calculator**, find the missing number in each of these calculations.

   a $20 - \square \times 2 = 10$ b $27 \div 3 + \square = 13$ c $\square - 45 \div 5 = 3$
   d $3 \times \square - 2 = 28$ e $20 - \square + 2 = 15$ f $8 + 12 \div \square = 10$
   g $\square \div 4 \div 2 = 2$ h $\square + 3 \times 3 = 16$

4 **Without using a calculator**, work out:

   a $5 \times (10 - 5)$ b $5 \times 10 - 5$ c $(9 + 6) \div 3$
   d $9 + 6 \div 3$ e $20 \div (5 - 1)$ f $20 \div 5 - 1$
   g $14 - (1 + 3)$ h $14 - 1 + 3$

3 Solving problems

This lesson will help you to solve problems involving integers.

You can find the value of (3 + 4) × 2 with these calculator key presses:

(3 + 4) × 2

Exercise 3A

You need a copy of **N3.1 Resource sheet 3.1**.

Use the digits 1, 2, 3 and 4 with any of the four operations +, −, × and ÷ to make the numbers 1 to 30.

- Use each of the four digits once each time.
  You can use them in any order but must not repeat a digit.

- You can use any operation. You don't need to use all four operations and you can repeat an operation.

- Use brackets where they are needed.

Extension problem

Try to make the numbers from 30 to 40.

Exercise 3B

1   For each calculation, predict and write down the result your
    calculator will give. Check with your calculator.

a	16 − (4 − 3)	b	12 ÷ (6 − 2)
c	(5 + 3) × 3	d	(20 − 4) ÷ 2
e	(8 + 4) ÷ (2 + 1)	f	(8 + 4) ÷ 2 + 1
g	(5 + 1) × (6 − 3)	h	(5 + 1) × 6 − 3

(2) Put brackets in these to make them correct.

a $7 \times 5 - 3 = 32$ b $7 \times 5 - 3 = 14$ c $28 \div 7 - 3 = 7$

d $28 \div 7 - 3 = 1$ e $6 - 2 + 3 - 4 = 5$ f $6 - 2 + 3 - 4 = -3$

g $5 + 2 \times 6 - 3 = 14$ h $5 + 2 \times 6 - 3 = 21$

⊙ Points to remember

⊙ Always work out the calculation in brackets first.

⊙ After brackets, multiply and divide before you add and subtract.

4 Multiples and tests of divisibility

This lesson will help you to recognise multiples and work out squares and square roots.

A **multiple** of a number divides exactly by the number.
For example, the numbers 5, 10, 15, 20, 25, … are all multiples of 5.

You can find out whether a number is a multiple by using **tests of divisibility**.

A number is:

divisible by **2** if its last digit is 0, 2, 4, 6 or 8;

divisible by **3** if its digit sum is divisible by 3;

divisible by **4** if half of it is even, or if its last two digits are divisible by 4;

divisible by **5** if its last digit is 5 or 0;

divisible by **6** if it is divisible by 2 and divisible by 3;

divisible by **9** if its digit sum is divisible by 9;

divisible by **10** if its last digit is 0.

You can check for **divisibility** with your calculator.

Example 1   Is 338 divisible by 13?

$3\ 3\ 8 \div 1\ 3 =$ 26

The whole-number answer of 26 tells you that 338 is **divisible** by 13.

Example 2   Is 1257 divisible by 15?

 $1\ 2\ 5\ 7 \div 1\ 5 =$ 83.8

The answer is not a whole number. This tells you that 1257 is **not** divisible by 15.

Exercise 4

1) Write down:

  a   all the multiples of 10 between 16 and 53

  b   all the multiples of 3 between 11 and 20

  c   all the multiples of 5 between 47 and 67

  d   all the multiples of 7 between 20 and 34

2) Which of these numbers are multiples of 8?

        18   32   56
          68   72

3) Four of these numbers are multiples of 3 **and** multiples of 5.

    Which numbers are they?

        89   75
          45
       37   24
          30   60

4) Choose from the numbers in the box. Write:

  a   three numbers divisible by 10

  b   five multiples of 5

  c   eight numbers divisible by 2

  d   five multiples of 9

  e   six numbers divisible by 8

  f   two multiples of 13

  g   three numbers **not** divisible by 3

  h   five numbers divisible by 6

        120 75   60
              24   45
        63 16   117
              81   112
        130 96   72

5) Look at these number cards.

    Choose three cards to make an even number that is greater than 400.

6 **Use your calculator** to check these.

a Is 242 divisible by 7? b Is 568 divisible by 8? c Is 402 divisible by 6?

d Is 143 divisible by 11? e Is 546 divisible by 12? f Is 260 divisible by 16?

7 **Use your calculator** to work out the value of these.

a 12^2 b 1.5^2 c $\sqrt{256}$ d $\sqrt{361}$

e 3×9^2 f $567 \div 9^2$ g $(21 - 4)^2$ h $15^2 \div 30^2$

Extension problem

8 Steve has a pack of cards numbered from 1 to 20. He picks four different cards.
Exactly three of the four numbers are multiples of 5.
Exactly three of the four numbers are even numbers.
All four of the numbers add up to less than 40.
What could the numbers be?

Points to remember

⊙ A **multiple** of a number divides exactly by the number.

⊙ There are simple tests for divisibility by 2, 3, 4, 5, 9 and 10.

⊙ If a number is divisible by 6, it must be divisible by 2 and divisible by 3.

⊙ The **square** of a number is the number multiplied by itself.
   If the square of 9 is 81, then the **square root** of 81 is 9 ($9^2 = 81$, $\sqrt{81} = 9$).

⊙ Always square before you multiply, divide, add or subtract.

5 Factors, primes, HCF and LCM

This lesson will help you to find factors and multiples and to identify prime numbers.

The **factors** of a number are all the numbers that divide into it exactly.

Factors of 12 are 1, 2, 3, 4, 6 and 12. Factors of 17 are 1, 17.
Factors of 32 are 1, 2, 4, 8, 16, 32.

A **prime number** has exactly two factors, 1 and the number itself.

There is an infinite number of prime numbers: 2, 3, 5, 7, 11, 13, 17, 19, …

The number 1 is not a prime number and 2 is the only even prime number.

You can find the **highest common factor** (HCF) of two numbers by looking at lists of their factors.

Example 1

Find the HCF of 16 and 36.

The factors of 16 are **1**, **2**, **4**, 8 and 16.

The factors of 36 are **1**, **2**, 3, **4**, 6, 9, 12, 18 and 36.

1, 2 and 4 are in both lists but the highest of these is 4, so 4 is the HCF.

You can find the **lowest common multiple** (LCM) of two numbers by looking at lists of their multiples.

Example 2

Find the LCM of 8 and 12.

The multiples of 8 are 8, 16, 24, 32, 40, **48**, 56, 64, **72**, …

The multiples of 12 are 12, 24, 36, **48**, 60, **72**, 84, 96, …

48 and 72 are in both lists but the smallest of these is 48, so 48 is the LCM.

Did you know that…?

Prime numbers were first studied by the ancient Greeks. In about 200 BCE **Eratosthenes** devised a way of identifying prime numbers.

1	2	3	4	5	6	7	8	9	10
11	12	13	14	15	16	17	18	19	20
21	22	23	24	25	26	27	28	29	30
31	32	33	34	35	36	37	38	39	40
41	42	43	44	45	46	47	48	49	50
51	52	53	54	55	56	57	58	59	60
61	62	63	64	65	66	67	68	69	70
71	72	73	74	75	76	77	78	79	80
81	82	83	84	85	86	87	88	89	90
91	92	93	94	95	96	97	98	99	100

Sieve of Eratosthenes

Start with 2 and cross out all the multiples of 2 that are greater than 2.

Find the next number that is not crossed out, which is 3. Cross out all the multiples of 3 that are greater than 3.

Find the next number that is not crossed out, which is 5. Cross out all the multiples of 5 that are greater than 5.

Keep on going like this. The numbers that are not crossed out are the prime numbers.

Eratosthenes was born about 275 BCE. He was also famous for measuring the diameter of the Earth. He starved himself to death in 195 BCE because he had gone blind and was depressed.

1. Write down:

   a two factor pairs of 21

   b two factor pairs of 35

   c three factor pairs of 20

   d three factor pairs of 28

   e three factor pairs of 50

   f three factor pairs of 60

   g four factor pairs of 24

   h four factor pairs of 40

2. Write a factor of 60 that is bigger than 10 but smaller than 20.

3. What is the highest common factor (HCF) of 24 and 40?

4. What is the lowest common multiple (LCM) of 45 and 60?

5. Use the four digits 7, 5, 2, 1.
   Choose two digits each time to make these two-digit numbers.

   a an even number

   b a multiple of 9

   c a square number

   d a factor of 96

6. 126 is a three-digit number that has 2 and 7 as factors.
   Write another three-digit number which has 2 and 7 as factors.

7. a Which numbers less than 20 have an odd number of factors?

   b Find a number bigger than 50 with an odd number of factors.

Extension problems

8. 13 is a prime number. It can be written as the sum of two square numbers.

   $$13 = 4 + 9$$
   $$= 2^2 + 3^2$$

   Find some more prime numbers less than 100 that can be written as the sum of two square numbers.

Work with a partner. You need a pack of digit cards from 0 to 9.

$$\boxed{0}\;\boxed{1}\;\boxed{2}\;\boxed{3}\;\boxed{4}\;\boxed{5}\;\boxed{6}\;\boxed{7}\;\boxed{8}\;\boxed{9}$$

You can use the digit cards to make a prime numbers.

For example, you could use 1 and 3 to make the prime number 31.

Use all ten cards to make five different prime numbers.

The numbers can have any number of digits.

Points to remember

- The **factors** of a whole number are all the whole numbers that divide into it exactly.

- Factors occur in pairs. The factor pairs for 10 are 1×10 and 2×5.

- **Prime numbers** have only two different factors, themselves and 1. 1 is not a prime number.

- You can find the **highest common factor (HCF)** of two numbers by looking at lists of their factors.

- You can find the **lowest common multiple (LCM)** of two numbers by looking at lists of their multiples.

How well are you doing?

Positive and negative numbers

1. The temperature on 8 January was 2°C.
   On 9 January it was 6 degrees colder.
   What was the temperature on 9 January?

2. Subtract 3 from −5.

3. Add −4 and −6.

4. What number should you add to −3 to get the answer 4?

5. What is −6 − (−3)?

Order of operations and brackets

6. Find the value of:

   a $12 + 15 \div 3$ b $(2 \times 5)^2 - 1$

7. Put brackets in this number sentence to make it correct:
   $7 - 4 \times 8 - 6 = 6$

Multiples, factors and primes

8. Explain why 35 is not a prime number.

9. Write a multiple of 3 that is bigger than 100.

10. I am thinking of a two-digit number that is a multiple of 8.
    The digits add up to 6.
    What is the number?

Sequences and patterns

This unit will help you to:

◎ extend and find missing terms in number sequences;

◎ find a term from the previous term or from its position in a sequence;

◎ describe a rule for a sequence in words then using a letter symbol;

◎ recognise and explain patterns in sequences.

1 Sequences and rules

This lesson will help you to use simple rules to extend number sequences.

A **sequence** of numbers follows a **rule**.

The numbers in this sequence are called the **terms** of the sequence.

   3,   5,   7,   9,   …

3 is the 1st term, 5 is the 2nd term, and so on.

The **rule** to find the next term is 'add 2' to the previous term.

The 5th term is $9 + 2 = 11$, and the 6th term is $11 + 2 = 13$, and so on.

Exercise 1

1 Look at this sequence of numbers: 2,   5,   8,   11,   14,   17,   …
   a What is the 1st term?
   b What is the 3rd term?
   c What is the difference between the 1st term and the 2nd term?
   d What is the difference between the 2nd term and the 3rd term?
   e What is the difference between consecutive terms?
   f What is the rule?
   g Write the next three terms.

(2) Write the rule and the next four terms.

a 3, 7, 11, 15, ...

b 14, 24, 34, 44, ...

c 72, 65, 58, 51, ...

d 61, 56, 51, 46, ...

e 5, 14, 23, 32, ...

f 6, 3, 0, −3, ...

g 1, 3, 9, 27, ...

h 64, 32, 16, 8, ...

(3) Write whether each sequence is in ascending or descending order.

a 1, 4, 7, 10, 13, 16, ...

b 100, 90, 80, 70, 60, ...

c 1.295, 1.285, 1.275, 1.265, ...

d −5, −8, −11, −14, −17, −20, ...

(4) Write the next five terms of each of these sequences.

	1st term	Rule		1st term	Rule
a	1	add 7	b	5	add 7
c	100	subtract 3	d	10	subtract 3
e	3	multiply by 2	f	10	multiply by 2

(5) Write the rule and the next five terms.

a $\frac{1}{4}$, $\frac{1}{2}$, $\frac{3}{4}$, 1, ...

b 4, $3\frac{2}{3}$, $3\frac{1}{3}$, 3, ...

(6) Write the next five terms of each of these sequences. You may **use a calculator**.

	1st term	Rule		1st term	Rule
a	1	multiply by 2 and add 3	b	3	multiply by 3 and subtract 5
c	4	divide by 2 and add 8	d	1	multiply by 10 and subtract 5
e	10	multiply by 1.5 and add 1			

⊙ Points to remember

- ⊙ A **sequence** of numbers follows a rule.
- ⊙ You can work out the next term if you know the **rule**.
- ⊙ If the rule is 'add 2', then the number after 15 will be 17.

2 Finding missing terms

This lesson will help you to find missing terms in sequences.

When the step size of a sequence is always the same, you can work out the step size if you know two of the terms.

Example

This sequence has equal steps. 5, ☐, ☐, ☐, 37.
Find the missing terms.

There are four equal steps between 5 and 37.
The difference between 5 and 37 is 32.
Each step is $32 \div 4 = 8$.

Exercise 2

① In these sequences, the step size is always the same.
Copy each sequence. Fill in the missing terms.

a 1, 5, …, 13, 17, …, 25, …

b …, …, 15, …, 27, …, …, …

c 2, …, …, 35, 46, …, 68, …

d 85, 82, …, …, 73, …, …, …

e 1, …, …, 7, …, …, 13, …

f …, …, 4, …, 3, 2.5, 2, …

g 3.15, …, …, 3.45, …, 3.65, …

h 10, …, …, …, …, …, …, 59

② What term or terms could go between each pair of numbers?
Describe the rule you have used.

a 1, …, 9   b 1, …, 16

c 5, …, 21   d 4, …, 36

e 10, …, 20   f 16, …, 8

3 In each sequence, find the missing terms and the 50th term.

double + 4

Term	1st	2nd	3rd	4th	5th	6th	7th	8th	50th
Sequence A	6	8	10	12	14	16	18	20	...
Sequence B	...	8	13	18	23	28	33	38	...
Sequence C	...	...	18	26	...	42	50	...	...
Sequence D	...	...	25	...	47	...	...	80	...
Sequence E	...	11	...	23	...	...	41	...	...

Extension problem

4 Copy each sequence. Fill in the missing terms.

a $\frac{1}{8}$, $\frac{1}{4}$, $\frac{3}{8}$, $\frac{1}{2}$, $\frac{5}{8}$, $\frac{3}{4}$, $\frac{7}{8}$, ...

b $\frac{1}{7}$, ..., ..., ..., $1\frac{2}{7}$, $1\frac{4}{7}$, ..., ...

c -1, -2, -4, ..., ..., -32, ..., ...

Points to remember

⊙ If the step size is always the same, and there are 3 steps between two known terms, each step is $\frac{1}{3}$ of the difference between the two terms.

⊙ You can work out the next term in a sequence if you know the rule.

3 Sequences from patterns

This lesson will help you to generate sequences from patterns and find missing terms.

Here is a sequence of shapes using triangles:

   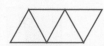

Pattern 1   Pattern 2   Pattern 3   Pattern 4
1 triangle   2 triangles   3 triangles   4 triangles

The **rule** to find the next pattern is 'add an extra triangle' to the previous pattern.

Pattern 5 is formed by adding a triangle to pattern 4.
There are 5 triangles in pattern 5.

Pattern 5
5 triangles

Exercise 3

1. Here is a sequence of patterns made up of crosses.
   The sequence continues in the same way.

   ```
   ×        × ×       × × ×      × × × ×
   ×        × ×       × × ×      × × × ×
   Pattern 1  Pattern 2  Pattern 3  Pattern 4
   ```

   a Write the rule for this sequence.   + 2

   b Draw pattern 5.

   c Copy and complete this table.

Pattern number	1	2	3	4	5	6	10	50
Number of crosses	2	4	6	8	10	12	20	100

   pattern no s × 2

2. Here is a sequence of triangles made from matchsticks.
   The sequence continues in the same way.

   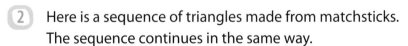

   Pattern 1   Pattern 2   Pattern 3

   a Write the rule for this sequence.   + 3

   b Copy and complete this table.

Pattern number	1	2	3	4	5	6	20	50
Number of matchsticks	3	6	9	12	15	18	60	150

   pattern no s × 3

③ Here is a sequence of patterns of red and green tiles.

　　　　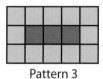

Pattern 1　　　　　　Pattern 2　　　　　　Pattern 3

a　How many red tiles will be in the 4th pattern?

b　How many red tiles will be in the 10th pattern?

c　How many green tiles will be in the 4th pattern?

d　How many green tiles will be in the 10th pattern?

e　Describe how the number of red tiles increases each time.

f　Describe how the number of green tiles increases each time.

g　How many red tiles will be in the 100th pattern?

h　How many green tiles will be in the 100th pattern?

i　Explain how to work out the number of green tiles in the 100th pattern.

④ Here is a pattern of pink and blue beads.

a　What colour is the 12th bead?　　　　b　What colour is the 29th bead?

c　What number is on the 8th pink bead?　　d　What number is on the 20th blue bead?

Extension problems

⑤ Here is a sequence of patterns made up of hexagons.

　　　　　　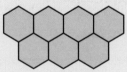

Pattern 1　　　　Pattern 2　　　　Pattern 3　　　　　Pattern 4

a　Write the rule for this sequence.

b　Copy and complete this table.

Pattern number	1	2	3	4	5	6
Number of hexagons	1	3	5	7		

c　Write the number of hexagons in pattern 20.

6 Here is a sequence of patterns made up of dots and squares.

  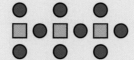 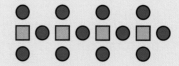

| Pattern 1 | Pattern 2 | Pattern 3 | Pattern 4 |

a Write the rule for the sequence of dots.

b Write the rule for the sequence of squares.

c Copy and complete the table.

Pattern number	1	2	3	4	5	6	10	100
Number of dots	3	6	9	12				
Number of squares	1	2	3	4				
Total number of dots and squares								

 Points to remember

⊙ You can make sequences from patterns of shapes that follow a rule.

⊙ Work out the pattern by looking at the way it increases or decreases.

4 Using a letter symbol

This lesson will help you to use letters to stand for numbers.

The **expression** $n + 5$ is an instruction telling you to 'add the number 5 to the number n'.

Examples

a There are n apples in a basket.
Jamie puts two more apples in the basket.
How many apples are now in the basket?

Since two apples are added to the basket, there are now $n + 2$ apples.

b There are n apples in a basket.
Lucy takes five of the apples in the basket.
How many apples are now in the basket?

Since five apples are taken from the basket, there are now $n - 5$ apples.

c Yousaf buys six apples. Each apple costs n pence.
Find the total cost of the six apples.

Since there are six apples, each one costing n pence,
the total cost is:

$$n + n + n + n + n + n$$
$$= 6 \times n$$
$$= 6n \text{ pence}$$

Exercise 4

1 **a** There are n people on a bus. Five more people get on the bus.
How many people are on the bus now?

    b There are n people on a bus. Two people get off the bus.
How many people are now on the bus?

    c There are n sweets in a jar.
Leroy eats 8 sweets.
How many sweets are now in the jar?

    d Each jar contains n sweets.
Write the total number of sweets in three jars.

    e There are six minibuses.
Each minibus has n passengers.
What is the total number of passengers?

    f Hilary buys 12 daffodils. Each daffodil costs d pence.
Find, in terms of d, the total cost of the 12 daffodils.

    g There are n people sitting at a table. Three more people join them.
How many people are sitting at the table now?

    h A minibus has n passengers. Half of them are children.
How many of the passengers are children?

2 Write these instructions in words.

    a $n + 9$ **b** $n + 12$ **c** $n - 5$ **d** $7 - n$

    e $n - 1$ **f** $-2 + n$ **g** $4n$ **h** $2n + 1$

(3) Copy and complete this table.

Expression	$n = 1$	$n = 2$	$n = 3$	$n = 4$	$n = 5$
$n + 7$	8				
$n - 1$		1			
$3n$					15
$2n + 3$	5				
$7n - 5$		9			

(4) Work out the value of n in each of these.

    a $n + 8 = 15$ **b** $n + 11 = 20$ **c** $n - 6 = 5$

Extension problem

(5) Write these instructions in words.

    a $4n$ **b** $\dfrac{n}{3}$ **c** $3n + 2$ **d** $5n - 3$

◉ Points to remember

- The **expression** $n + 5$ is an instruction telling you to 'add the number 5 to the number n'.
- When $n = 3$, $n + 5 = 8$.

5 Finding a term from its position

This lesson will help you to find a term from its position in the sequence.

If the **formula** for the term in the nth position is $3n + 2$ then:

    the 1st term is $3 \times 1 + 2 = 5$,

    the 2nd term is $3 \times 2 + 2 = 8$,

    the 3rd term is $3 \times 3 + 2 = 11$.

1 Look at this number sequence:

6, 12, 18, 24, 30, 36, 42, 48, 54, ...

The sequence continues in the same way.

a Describe the number sequence.

b What is the 4th term?

c What is the 10th term?

d What is the 17th term?

e Explain how you could work out the 35th term of the sequence.

f Write the formula for the nth term of the sequence.

2 Write the next five terms of each sequence using the formula for the nth term.

	nth term	Sequence		nth term	Sequence
a	$10n$	10, 20, ...	b	$5n + 1$	6, 11, ...
c	$7n - 2$	5, 12, ...	d	$2n + 9$	11, 13, ...
e	$11n - 5$	6, 17, ...	f	$2n - 6$	-4, -2, ...

3 a What is the 9th term of the sequence $3n + 5$?

b What is the 10th term of the sequence $7n + 4$?

c What is the 7th term of the sequence $6n - 1$?

d What is the 4th term of the sequence $9n - 7$?

Extension problems

4 a What is the 100th term of the sequence $13n - 5$?

b What is the 200th term of the sequence $0.5n + 2$?

5 Write the next five terms of each sequence using the formula for the nth term.

	nth term	Sequence
a	$0.5n + 1$	1.5, 2, ...
b	$\frac{1}{4}n + \frac{1}{4}$	$\frac{1}{2}$, $\frac{3}{4}$, ...

◉ Points to remember

- ⊙ You can work out any term in a sequence if you know the formula for the **nth term.**

- ⊙ If the formula for the nth term is $3n + 1$, then the 9th term is $3 \times 9 + 1 = 28$.

How well are you doing?

Can you:

- extend and find missing terms in number sequences?
- find a term from the previous term or from its position in a sequence?
- describe a rule for a sequence in words then using a letter symbol?
- recognise and explain patterns in sequences?

Sequences and patterns

1 *2007 level 4*

The rule for this sequence is to add the same number each time.

3, □, □, □, 19

Write the three missing numbers.

2 *2003 level 4*

a The number chain below is part of a doubling number chain.
Copy the chain and fill in the missing numbers.

$\ldots \rightarrow 40 \rightarrow 80 \rightarrow 160 \rightarrow \ldots$

b The number chain below is part of a halving number chain.
Copy the chain and fill in the missing numbers..

$40 \rightarrow 20 \rightarrow 10 \rightarrow \ldots \rightarrow \ldots$

3 *2003 level 4*

a I think of a number. I call my number n. | n

Then I add 5 to my number. | $n + 5$

The answer is 8. | $n + 5 = 8$

What was my number?

b Solve this equation to find the value of m. | $m - 2 = 8$

4 *2006 level 4*

Jo places equilateral triangles in straight lines to make this sequence.

 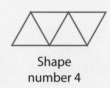

| Shape number 1 | Shape number 2 | Shape number 3 | Shape number 4 |

Look at the table below.

Shape number	1	2	3	4
Perimeter	3 cm	4 cm	5 cm	6 cm

Jo makes shape number 15. What is the perimeter of shape number 15?

5 *2005 level 4*

Kerry makes a pattern from blue tiles and white tiles.
You cannot see all of the pattern but it continues in the same way.

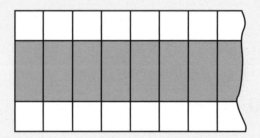

a   Kerry uses 30 blue tiles. How many white tiles does she use?

b   Tim makes a pattern like Kerry's but he uses 64 white tiles.
    How many blue tiles does Tim use?

Whole numbers and decimals

This unit will help you to:

- understand the value of digits in decimals and put decimals in order;
- multiply and divide by 10, 100 or 1000;
- calculate with whole numbers, decimals, money and measures;
- solve number problems and explain your solutions;
- use rounding to estimate and check answers.

1 Place value

This lesson will help you to use place value, and multiply and divide by 10, 100 or 1000.

 Did you know that...?

Al'Khwarizmi lived from about 780 to 850. He studied at the School of Wisdom run by the Caliph of Baghdad. He wrote a book which showed ways of doing sums using place value. In Latin, his book was called *Liber Algorismi*.

He also wrote the first book ever to be written on algebra.

Today, his name is used in the word *algorithm*, which is a way of doing a written calculation.

Mohammed al-Khwarizmi

When you **multiply** a whole number or decimal:
- by 10, its digits move 1 place to the left, e.g. $0.56 \times 10 = 5.6$;
- by 100, its digits move 2 places to the left, e.g. $0.56 \times 100 = 56$;
- by 1000, its digits move 3 places to the left, e.g. $0.56 \times 1000 = 560$.

When you **divide** a whole number or decimal:
- by 10, the digits move 1 place to the right, e.g. $75 \div 10 = 7.5$;
- by 100, the digits move 2 places to the right, e.g. $75 \div 100 = 0.75$;
- by 1000, the digits move 3 places to the right, e.g. $75 \div 1000 = 0.075$.

1 Write these in figures.

   a six thousand and fifty

   b ten thousand, five hundred

   c two hundred thousand and five

   d one million, sixty thousand and ten

2 Write these in words.

   a 20 405   b 607 050   c 2 040 300   d 520 020

3 Make the biggest possible odd number using each digit once.

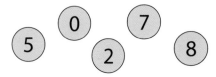

4 Make the smallest possible even number using each digit once.

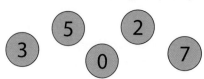

5 Copy and complete these multiplication calculations.

   a 46 × 100 = ...   b 8.3 × ... = 830   c 0.2 × ... = 2

   d 320 × 100 = ...   e 5.9 × 1000 = ...   f 0.03 × 10 = ...

   g 0.004 × ... = 0.04   h 1.07 × ... = 1070

6 Copy and complete these division calculations.

   a 72 ÷ 100 = ...   b 9.1 ÷ ... = 0.91   c 0.5 ÷ ... = 0.05

   d 560 ÷ 100 = ...   e 3.7 ÷ 1000 = ...   f 0.08 ÷ 10 = ...

   g 4 ÷ ... = 0.004   h 2.6 ÷ ... = 0.026

7 Copy and complete these multiplication and division calculations.

   a 6050 ÷ 100 = ...   b 0.9 × ... = 900   c 5.1 × ... = 51

   d 4002 ÷ 1000 = ...   e 7 ÷ 10 = ...   f 3200 × 1000 = ...

   g 82 030 ÷ 1000 = ...   h 830 ÷ ... = 8.3

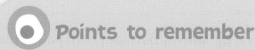

Points to remember

- $0.3 = \frac{3}{10}$ $0.09 = \frac{9}{100}$ $0.004 = \frac{4}{1000}$
- When a whole number or decimal is:
  - multiplied by 10, its digits move 1 place to the left;
  - multiplied by 100, its digits move 2 places to the left;
  - multiplied by 1000, its digits move 3 places to the left.

- When a whole number or decimal is:
  - divided by 10, the digits move 1 place to the right;
  - divided by 100, the digits move 2 places to the right;
  - divided by 1000, the digits move 3 places to the right.

2 Ordering and rounding

This lesson will help you to order and round decimals, and estimate answers to calculations.

The position of a digit in a number affects its value. Each place after the decimal point has a value one tenth of the value of the place to its left.

In the number **4.763**, the value of the digit **4** is four, the value of the digit **7** is seven tenths, the value of the digit **6** is six hundredths, and the value of the digit **3** is three thousandths.

Example 1
$$4.763 = 4 + 0.7 + 0.06 + 0.03$$
$$= 4 + \frac{7}{10} + \frac{6}{10} + \frac{3}{1000}$$

When you round whole numbers, if the first unwanted digit is 5, 6, 7, 8 or 9, add 1 to the last digit that you keep. Then replace all the unwanted digits by zeros.

Example 2
5621 to the nearest 100 is 5600;
29 900 to the nearest 1000 is 30 000

When you round decimals, if the first unwanted digit is 5, 6, 7, 8 or 9, add 1 to the last digit that you keep. Then leave off all the unwanted digits.

Example 3
2.346 correct to two decimal places is 2.35
9.795 correct to one decimal place is 9.8

1 Write the number that is exactly halfway between each pair of numbers.

a 3 and 6   b 2.5 and 4.5

c 3.25 and 4.25   d 0.25 and 1.75

e 6.75 and 7.75   f 2.5 and 5

2 Write each set of numbers in order, starting with the smallest.

a 663   6361   61 316   6631   b 7407   7704   7470   7740

c 18.18   118.1   18.81   18.11   d 0.25   0.52   0.5   0.2

e 1.01   1.001   1.101   0.11   f 0.27   0.207   0.027   2.07   2.7

3 Round these numbers to the nearest 10.

a 85   b 206   c 4812   d 299

4 Round these numbers to the nearest 100.

a 550   b 4320   c 17 408   d 999

5 Round these numbers to the nearest 1000.

a 7567   b 29 900   c 38 200   d 4 237 256

6 Round these numbers to the nearest whole number.

a 14.687   b 0.551   c 231.35   d 9.72

7 Round these numbers to one decimal place.

a 14.16   b 0.051   c 2.838   d 20.984

◉ Points to remember

⊙ Round up 'halfway' numbers.

Example: 42.**5** rounds up to 43, and 86**5**0 rounds up to 8700.

⊙ Use rounding to estimate answers to calculations.

Example: 4.8×6.2 is approximately $5 \times 6 = 30$.

3 Mental calculations

This lesson will help you to use mental methods to calculate with whole numbers and decimals.

A number line helps you to work out sums and differences.
Deal with the whole-number part first.

Example 1

Work out: **a** 2.4 + 3.7   **b** 8.4 − 5.6

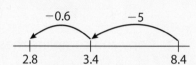

Use the facts that you know to work out new facts.

Example 2

Work out 3.5 ÷ 7.

Since 35 ÷ 7 = 5, 3.5 ÷ 7 = 5 ÷ 10 = 0.5

Exercise 3

1 As you go up the pyramid, each number is
the sum of the two numbers below it.

Copy and complete these pyramids.

a
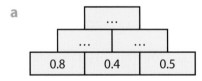

b
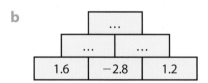

c
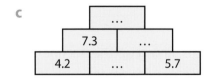

d
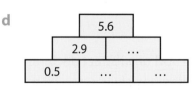

2 Copy and complete these multiplication calculations.

   a 0.3 × 4 = ...   **b** 0.07 × 6 = ...   **c** 0.002 × 7 = ...

   d 0.6 × 5 = ...   **e** 0.05 × 8 = ...   **f** 0.009 × 9 = ...

   g 0.09 × 8 = ...   **h** 0.004 × 5 = ...

3. In these arithmagons, the number in each square is the sum of the two numbers on either side of it.

Copy and complete these arithmagons.

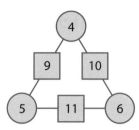

a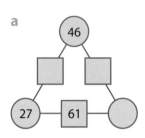

b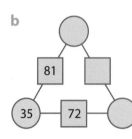

c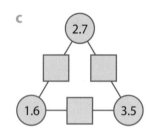

d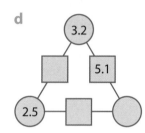

4. Copy and complete these division calculations.

a $4.2 \div 7 = ...$ b $0.35 \div 5 = ...$ c $0.036 \div 9 = ...$

d $2.0 \div 5 = ...$ e $0.48 \div 8 = ...$ f $0.009 \div 3 = ...$

g $0.012 \div 6 = ...$ h $0.04 \div 8 = ...$

● Points to remember

⊙ There are often different ways of doing mental calculations.
Choose a method that you understand and that works best for you.

⊙ When a mental calculation has more than one step, jot down the answer to each step as you go along.

4 Written calculations

This lesson will help you to use written methods to calculate and solve problems involving whole numbers and decimals, and to check your results.

You can add or subtract decimals by writing numbers in columns, lining up the decimal points. If you wish, you can fill gaps at the end of the decimal places with zeros.

Example 1: $5.26 + 13.8$

$$
\begin{array}{r}
5.26 \\
+13.80 \\
\hline
19.06 \\
\end{array}
$$
  1

Example 2: $6.2 - 1.58$

$$
\begin{array}{r}
{}^{5}\!6.{}^{11}2\,{}^{1}0 \\
-1.58 \\
\hline
4.62 \\
\end{array}
$$

1. Work out these calculations.

   a 32.6 + 18.73   b 12.8 − 3.45

   c 0.3 + 1.27 + 9.6   d 6.08 − 3.16

   e 76.58 + 314.5 + 9.08 f 1.2 + 3.41 − 4.56

2. A water tank holds 500 litres.
   How much is left in the tank if 153.8 litres is taken out of it?

3. What is the total cost of:
   a newspaper at 78p,
   a magazine at £2.56
   and a paperback at £3.88?

4. How much change do you get from £20 for:
   a puzzle book at £5.25,
   some stickers at 80p
   and a pack of felt pens at £1.92?

5. From Stoke to Tadley is 5.7 km.
   From Tadley to Burnside is 12.375 km.
   How far is the journey from Stoke to Tadley to Burnside?

6. Sarah has a 5 kg bag of potatoes.
   She uses 672 grams of the potatoes.
   What is the weight of the potatoes left in the bag?

7. What is the total cost of two loaves at 82p each, six cakes at 30p each,
   four buns at 22p each and one flan at 75p?

8. Ramesh has 7.3 metres of rope. He cuts off 163 centimetres.
   How much of the rope is left?

Multiplying whole numbers

To multiply, use an efficient method that works best for you.
In the long multiplication method, you can multiply by the tens or units first.

36 × 47   Estimate: 40 × 50 = 2000

Method 1: Grid method

×	30	6
40	1200	240
7	210	42

```
  1200
   240
   210
+   42
  1692
```

Answer: 36 × 47 = 1692

Method 2: Long multiplication

```
    36
  × 47
  1440   40 × 36
   252   7 × 36
  1692   47 × 36
```

```
    36
  × 47
   252   7 × 36
  1440   40 × 36
  1692   47 × 36
```

Answer: 36 × 47 = 1692

Exercise 4B

1 Table-tennis balls are packed in boxes of 64.
   A sports shop buys 36 boxes.
   How many table-tennis balls are there in 36 boxes?

2 89 pupils are going on a visit to France.
   Each pupil pays £153.
   How much money do the pupils pay for the visit in total?

3 A printer for a computer weighs 28 kg.
   A delivery van has 27 of the printers on board.
   What is the total weight of the printers on the van?

4 A digital TV costs £674. A store buys 25 of the TVs to sell on the Internet.
   How much does the store pay for the TVs?

Extension problem

5 Copy and complete the calculations below.
   Choose from the numbers on the right to go in the boxes.

19	32	56
68	72	245

a ☐ × ☐ = 2304   b ☐ × ☐ = 1064   c ☐ × ☐ = 3808

d ☐ × ☐ = 1292   e ☐ × ☐ = 7840   f ☐ × ☐ = 4655

g (☐ + ☐) × ☐ = 7200   h 1000 − (☐ × ☐) = 392

Points to remember

- For column addition and subtraction of decimals:
  - line up the decimal points, write tenths under tenths, hundredths under hundredths, and so on;
  - fill the gaps at the end of the decimal places with zeros if you wish;
  - show 'carry' figures clearly;
  - change units of measurement to the same unit.

- For multiplication of whole numbers in columns:
  - estimate the answer first;
  - line up units under units, tens under tens, and so on;
  - compare the answer with the estimate.

5 Using a calculator

This lesson will help you to:

- use a calculator to work with decimals, money and metric measure;

- solve word problems and interpret calculator results in the context of the problem.

Look at the expression $\frac{362 + 54}{98 - 82}$.

The line between the top and the bottom acts as a division sign ($\div$) or as brackets. You can write the expression as:

$(362 + 54) \div (98 - 82)$

You can key it into your calculator as:

$(\ 3 \ 6 \ 2 \ + \ 5 \ 4 \ ) \ \div \ (\ 9 \ 8 \ - \ 8 \ 2 \ )$

Exercise 5

1. **Use your calculator** to work out these calculations.

   a $\dfrac{193 + 867}{212}$ b $\dfrac{212 + 74}{73 - 29}$ c $\dfrac{122 + 98}{65 - 15}$

   d $\dfrac{24 \times 642}{97 - 25}$ e $\dfrac{863 + 97}{16 \times 24}$ f $\dfrac{2448 \div 36}{15 + 19}$

   g $8.3 - (4.2 - 1.9)$ h $15.6 + (3.2 - 1.7)^2$

(2) Ajit has three supermarket bills.

Butter	£1.00
Soup	£0.50
Burgers	£2.67
Eggs	£2.11
Milk	£0.68
Lemonade	£1.23
Bread	£0.89
Chicken	£5.23
Oranges	£0.70
Total	**£64.68**

Butter	£1.10
Soup	£0.65
Burgers	£2.67
Eggs	£1.99
Milk	£0.68
Lemonade	£1.18
Bread	£0.89
Chicken	£5.15
Oranges	£0.70
Total	**£55.90**

Butter	£1.00
Soup	£0.76
Burgers	£2.54
Eggs	£2.07
Milk	£0.68
Lemonade	£1.06
Bread	£0.89
Chicken	£5.23
Oranges	£0.78
Total	**£49.05**

a Ajit estimates the total amount of all three bills.
He rounds each bill to the nearest £10 and adds them up. What total does he get?

b Nasreen works out the actual total of all three bills.
What is the difference between her total and Ajit's total?

(3) Jade buys a sun hat at £3.29 and some sunglasses at £4.69.
How much change does she get from £10?

(4) A pot of yogurt costs 45p.
How many yogurts can you buy for £5?

(5) A packet of goldfish food contains 2 kilograms.
Rachel feeds her goldfish 40 grams of food each day.
How many days does the packet of food last?

(6) **a** Harry has to travel 145 miles for work each day.
How far does Harry travel in 28 days?

b Harry gets paid 35p per mile for his travel expenses.
How much does he get for travel expenses for 28 days?

(7) **Use your calculator** for this investigation.

41 and 28 are a special pair of numbers.

Work out 41 × 28. Work out 14 × 82.
What do you notice?

Work out 93 × 13. Work out 13 × 91.
What do you notice?

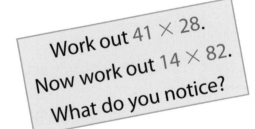

Work out 41 × 28.
Now work out 14 × 82.
What do you notice?

Try 48 × 63 and 84 × 36.

Try 26 × 31 and 62 × 13.

Try some more multiplications in the same way. Find some more special pairs of two-digit numbers that give the same product when reversed.

What is the relationship between the digits in these special pairs of numbers?

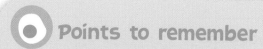

Points to remember

When you use a calculator:

- ⊙ estimate the result of a calculation and check the answer against the estimate;
- ⊙ check a one-step calculation by working the problem backwards;
- ⊙ use the CLEAR-ALL key before each new calculation;
- ⊙ use the CLEAR KEY to clear the last entry.

6 Problem solving

This lesson will help you to solve number problems, explain your solutions, and interpret calculator results in the context of the problem.

 Did you know that...?

Some mathematical problems appear simple but are difficult to solve without a calculator or computer to help you.

For example, in 1853, **Francis Guthrie** was colouring a map of the counties in England. He wanted counties that are next to each other to be a different colour. He spotted that he needed only four colours to colour the whole map.

It took until 1976 for mathematicians in the USA to prove that any map could be coloured using at most four colours. They used a computer program to test every possible type of map.

Exercise 6A

1. Do this question **without using your calculator**.
   In these sequences, the same number is added each time.
   Copy the sequences and write the next four terms.

   a 7.94   7.96   7.98   ...   .

   b 8.45   8.47   8.49   ...   .

   c 5.91   5.95   5.99   ...   .

   d 1.96   1.99   2.02   ...   .

   e 2.93   2.96   2.99   ...   .

Use your calculator. Record the key presses you make.

1 Make your calculator display the number 100 by using only the keys below.

(3)(7)(+)(−)(=)

Since 3 + 7 = 10, by adding ten 3s and ten 7s, you can get a total of 100.
Make 100 with fewer key presses.

2 Make your calculator display the number 1000 by using only the keys below.

(2)(7)(−)(×)(=)

Hint: You could aim to make a number just over 1000, then use subtraction to reduce the answer to 1000.

3 Use only these keys.

(1)(0)(+)(=)(·)

Make each of these numbers. Press as few keys as possible.

a 0.12   b 2.4   c 0.33   d 1.04   e 2.21

4 In these calculations, the signs +, −, × or ÷ have been replaced with a ●.
Rewrite the calculations, replacing each ● with the correct sign.

a 17 ● 17 ● 17 = 306   b 38 ● 58 ● 47 = 49

c (47 ● 53) ● 10 = 1000   d 27 ● 5 ● 5 = 675

e (437 ● 2) ● 126 = 1000   f 91 ● 7 ● 13 = 49

5 In these calculations, each ★ stands for a missing digit. Find the missing digits.

a 1★★ × 23 = 3013   b 36 × 4★ = 169★

● Points to remember

When you solve problems using your calculator:

◉ work systematically;

◉ keep a careful record of your findings as you go along;

◉ look for patterns and use them to explain your conclusions.

How well are you doing?

Whole numbers and decimals (no calculator)

1. How many hundreds are there in ten thousand?

2. Work out:

   a 0.367×1000

   b $580 \div 1000$

3. Write a number that is bigger than 0.3 but smaller than 0.4.

4. Put these numbers in order of size, starting with the smallest:

   0.17   0.7   0.071   0.107

5. Round:

   a 56 275 to the nearest 100

   b 5.096 to one decimal place

6. Subtract 1.9 from 2.7.

7. Estimate the answer to 9.85×14.16.

8. Calculate:

   a $51.7 - 3.48$

   b 364×57

Whole numbers and decimals (calculator allowed)

9. **Use a calculator** to calculate:

   a $100 - (22.75 + 19.08)$

   b $49.3 \times (2.06 + 8.5)$

10. In these calculations, each $\star$ stands for a missing digit. Find the missing digits.

    a $\star 3 \times 59 = 767$

    b $1\star \times \star 9 = 4\star 6$

Area and perimeter

This unit will help you to:

- know formulae for the area and the perimeter of a rectangle;
- work out the area and perimeter of shapes made from rectangles;
- work out the surface area of cuboids;
- imagine 3D shapes and recognise some of their properties;
- solve problems involving measurements.

1 Area and perimeter of rectangles

This lesson will help you to use formulae for the area and perimeter of a rectangle.

The **perimeter** of a 3D shape is the total distance around its edge.

The perimeter of the rectangle on the right is:

50 + 40 + 50 + 40 = 180 cm

Perimeter of a rectangle = 2 × length + 2 × width

Perimeters are measured in units of length, such as:

millimetres (mm)
centimetres (cm)
metres (m)
kilometres (km)

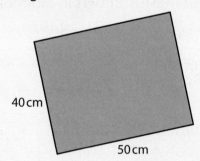

The **area** of a 2D shape is the amount of surface it covers.

Area of a rectangle = length × width

The area of the rectangle on the right is:

15 × 10 = 150 m²

Areas are measured in square units, such as:

square millimetres (mm²)
square centimetres (cm²)
square metres (m²)
square kilometres (km²)

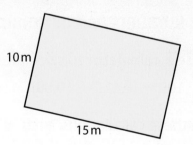

1 Work with a partner. Look at these rectangles.

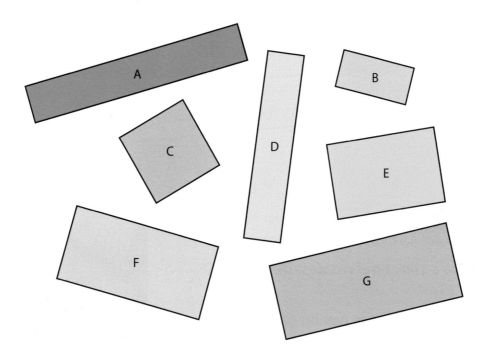

For each rectangle:

a **estimate** the perimeter and area;

b **measure** the sides and calculate the perimeter and area.

Your teacher will ask you for your estimates and measurements, and will record them in a table like this one.

Shape	Perimeter		Area	
	Estimate	Actual	Estimate	Actual
A				
B				
C				
D				
E				
F				
G				

(2) Calculate the area and perimeter of each of these rectangles.

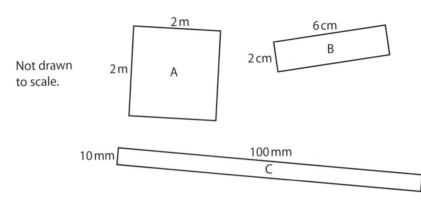

Not drawn to scale.

A: 2 m × 2 m

B: 6 cm × 2 cm

C: 100 mm × 10 mm

(3) Atul wants to repaint his rectangular garage door. It measures 4.5 m wide by 2.5 m high.

Atul has a 2 litre tin of red gloss paint that will cover 25 m².

Is this enough paint to give his garage doors two coats of paint?

(4) The perimeter of a rectangle is 300 mm. Its length is 8 cm.

What is the area of the rectangle?

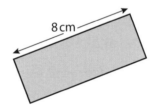

8 cm

(5) The area of a square is 25 m². Find its perimeter.

(6) Jonathan wants to tile his kitchen floor.

The floor is a square that measures 4 m by 4 m.

a What is the perimeter of the kitchen floor?

b What is the area of the kitchen floor?

One floor tile measures 33 cm by 33 cm.

c What is the least number of floor tiles needed to tile the floor?

d The tiles are sold in boxes of 9.
How many boxes of tiles should Jonathan buy?

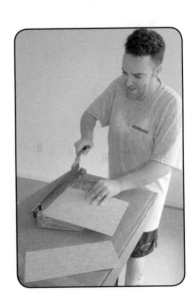

Extension problems

7 **a** This 4 by 4 square is divided into four pieces of equal area.
Each piece must be the same shape.

Investigate different ways of doing it.

b Now do it so that each of the pieces is a different shape.

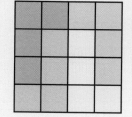

8 The area of a rectangle is 36 mm². The perimeter is 30 mm.
Find the length and width of the rectangle.

 Points to remember

- **Perimeter** is the distance around the outside of a shape.
- **Area** is a measure of the surface covered by a shape.
- Area is always measured in square units.
- Area of a rectangle = length × width.
- Change units of length to the same unit before you do any calculations.
- Shapes that have the same area may not have the same perimeter.

---

2 Irregular shapes

 Did you know that…?

Being able to find the biggest area you can enclose with a fixed length is useful. For example, a farmer who has a fixed length of fencing might want to know the biggest area of field he can make for his chickens.

Dido, the daughter of the King of Tyre in Greece, is said to have solved a similar problem in the 8th century BCE.

Dido wanted to buy some land on the north coast of Africa. She was told she could have as much land as she could surround with the skin of an ox.

She cut the skin into a long thin strip and then enclosed a huge semicircle as the biggest area she could get.

This lesson will help you to find the area and perimeter of some irregular shapes.

Example 1

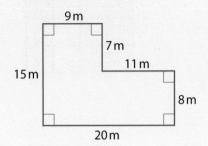

Here is a diagram of a garden.
How much fencing is needed to go around its perimeter?

The perimeter is the sum of the lengths of all the edges.

Perimeter = 15 + 9 + 7 + 11 + 8 + 20 = 70 m

Example 2

The diagram shows the floor plan of a room.
Work out the area of the floor.

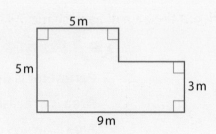

Divide the shape into two rectangles A and B.

The area of rectangle A is $5 \times 5 = 25$ m²
The area of rectangle B is $4 \times 3 = 12$ m²

Total area = Area A + Area B = 25 + 12 = 37 m²

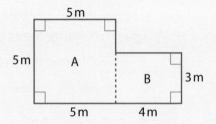

Exercise 2

You may **use your calculator** when necessary. You will need dotty paper.

1   On dotty paper, make at least six different shapes with
    a perimeter of 12 units.

    The example on the right has an area of 5 square units.

    Find the area of each of your shapes.
    Which of your shapes has the greatest area?

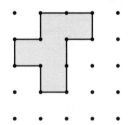

2   This diagram shows the plan of a floor.
    a   Work out the perimeter of the floor.
    b   Work out the area of the floor.

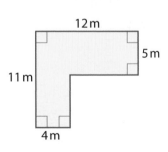

3 Work out the perimeters of these shapes. All the corners are right angles.

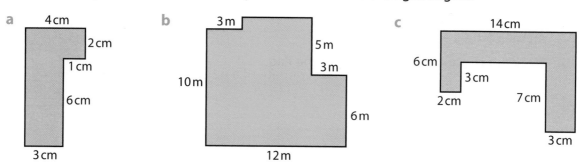

a 4 cm, 2 cm, 1 cm, 6 cm, 3 cm

b 3 m, 5 m, 3 m, 10 m, 6 m, 12 m

c 14 cm, 6 cm, 3 cm, 2 cm, 7 cm, 3 cm

4 Work out the area of each shape. All the corners are right angles.

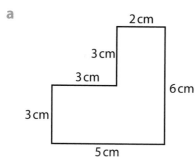

a 2 cm, 3 cm, 3 cm, 3 cm, 6 cm, 5 cm

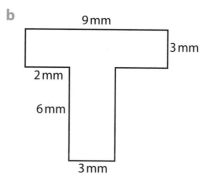

b 9 mm, 3 mm, 2 mm, 6 mm, 3 mm

5 Work out the shaded area of each shape. All the corners are right angles.

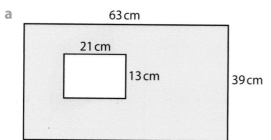

a 63 cm, 21 cm, 13 cm, 39 cm

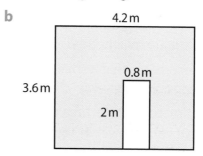

b 4.2 m, 0.8 m, 3.6 m, 2 m

6 The width of each blue strip on this flag is 30 cm. All the corners are right angles.

Work out the area of the blue part of the flag.

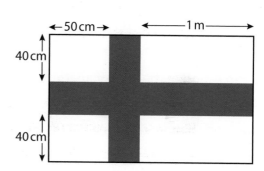

50 cm, 1 m, 40 cm, 40 cm

7 This flag is 150 cm wide by 90 cm high.
The width of each red strip is 18 cm.
All the corners are right angles.

Work out the area of the red part of the flag.

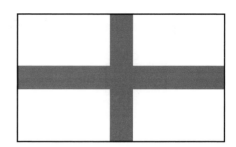

Extension problem

8 A square on this 3 by 3 pinboard has an area of 1 square unit.

Explain why the blue shape has an area of 2 square units.

Find six different shapes with an area of 2 square units
on a 3 by 3 pinboard. Record each new shape on dotty paper.

9 The area of a small orange leaf is about 8.5 cm².

a What is the approximate area of the leaf
in square millimetres?

b Li estimates that a small orange tree has
1000 leaves like this.
Estimate the total area of the tree's leaves.
Give your answer in square metres.

⦿ Points to remember

- ⦿ You can estimate the area of an irregular shape by counting squares.
- ⦿ Divide a shape into smaller shapes to help find its area.
- ⦿ There is often more than one way to divide a shape.
- ⦿ Make sure that all the units are the same before you do any calculations.

3 Surface area of cuboids

This lesson will help you to find the surface area of cuboids.

The **surface area** of a cuboid is the sum of the areas of all its faces.

A cube is a special cuboid.

The diagram shows a cube. Each edge is 2 cm long.
Each of its six faces is a square.

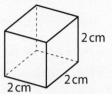

The area of each square face is $2 \times 2 = 4\,cm^2$.
So the surface area of the cube is $6 \times 4 = 24\,cm^2$.

Exercise 3

1 The squares on the outside of a cube are painted dark blue,
   light blue and white, as shown on the diagram.

   a How many squares are coloured dark blue?

   b How many squares are coloured light blue?

   c How many squares are coloured white?

2 Calculate the surface area of this cuboid.

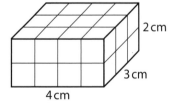

3 Calculate the surface area of each of these cuboids.

   a
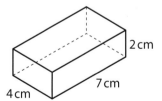

   b
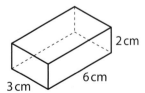

   c
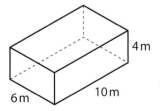

   d
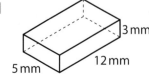

(4) Work out the surface area of each of these cuboids.

    a 40 cm by 30 cm by 20 cm

    b 20 m by 7 m by 5 m

    c 5 mm by 10 mm by 8 mm

(5) Sugar cubes have edges of 1 cm.
They are individually wrapped in paper with no overlaps.

There are 24 sugar cubes in a packet.
How much wrapping paper is needed altogether to wrap all 24 cubes?

(6) This shape is made from three identical cubes.
Each cube has an edge length of 4 cm.

Calculate the surface area of the complete shape.

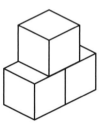

Extension problems

(7) The surface area of a cuboid is 76 mm².
It has a height of 2 mm and a length of 5 mm. What is its width?

(8) The areas of three of the faces of this cuboid are
shown on the diagram.

    a Calculate the total surface area of the cuboid.

    b What are the dimensions of the cuboid?

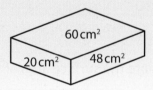

● Points to remember

⊙ To find the **surface area** of a shape, add the areas of all its faces.

⊙ Surface area is measured in square units, e.g. mm², cm², m² and km² for metric units.

⊙ When you work out surface area of a cuboid, change the lengths of the edges to the same units.

4 3D shapes

This lesson will help you to imagine 3D shapes and recognise some of their properties.

You can draw a cube on triangular dotty paper like this.

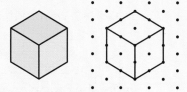

Exercise 4

1   There are seven different ways of arranging four identical cubes touching face-to-face.

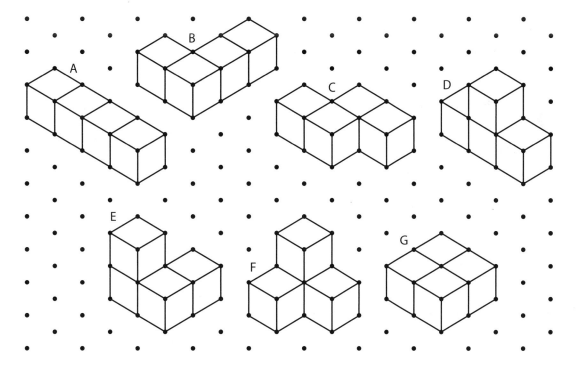

Each face of a cube has an area of 1 square unit.

a   Work out the surface area of each of the shapes A to G.
    Use the shapes you have made in class to help you.

b   Which shape has the least surface area?

c   How many pairs of touching faces does each shape have?

② How many cubes do you need to make each of these shapes?

a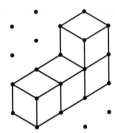

b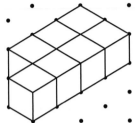

c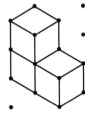

d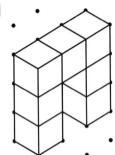

e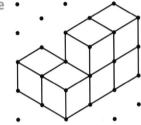

f

③ Each of the cubes in question 2 is 1 cm by 1 cm by 1 cm.

What is the surface area of each shape?

You can use cubes to make the shape to help you work out its surface area.

Extension problem

④ How many pairs of touching faces are there in each of the shapes in question 2?

⊙ **Points to remember**

⊙ To find the surface area of a shape, add the areas of all its faces.
⊙ Surface area is measured in square units, e.g. mm², cm², m².
⊙ You can represent a shape made from cubes on triangular dotty paper.

How well are you doing?

Area and perimeter

1 Here is a 1 cm square grid.

Some of the grid is shaded.

What area is shaded?

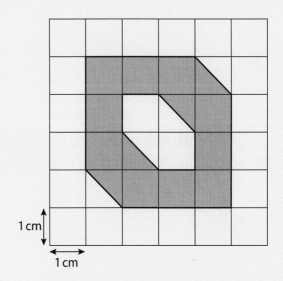

2 a What is the perimeter of this shape?

   b What is the area of this shape?

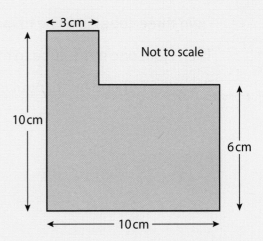

3D shapes and surface area

3 This cuboid is made from centimetre cubes.

It is 4 centimetres by 3 centimetres
by 2 centimetres.

What is the surface area of the cuboid?

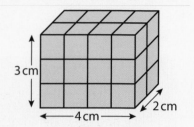

4 *2006 level 4*

Sam uses 8 cubes to make this shape.

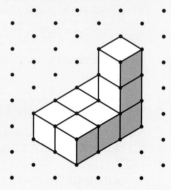

He adds more cubes to make this cuboid.
How many more cubes does he add to make this cuboid?

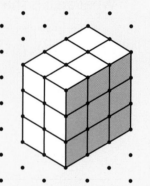

5 *2003 level 4*

I join three cubes in a line to make this shape.

Then I join one more cube to make an L-shape.

Draw the L-shape on triangular dotty paper.

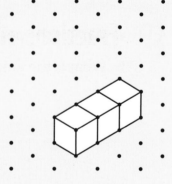

Fractions and percentages

This unit will help you to:

- use fractions to describe and compare parts of shapes;
- find equivalent fractions, decimals and percentages;
- work out fractions and percentages of numbers, money and measures;
- add and subtract simple fractions;
- multiply a fraction by a whole number;
- solve number problems, check your answers and explain your methods.

Did you know that...?

The ancient city of Uruk was the world's first city. It dates from more than 5000 years ago.

The people of Uruk had many different ways of writing numbers. One system was used for counting animals. A different system was for counting cheeses. Another system was used to count baskets of grain and included fractions. There were other systems for weights, areas and time, and so on.

The systems were often changed. Numbers for fractions and counting baskets of grain changed every time the size of the baskets changed!

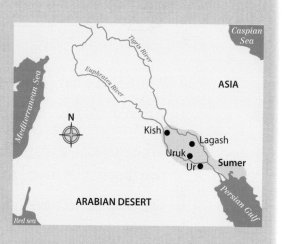

1 Fractions of shapes

This lesson will help you to use fractions to describe and compare parts of shapes.

This shape is divided into seven equal triangles.

$\frac{3}{7}$ of this shape is shaded red. $\frac{4}{7}$ is shaded yellow.

The whole shape is $\frac{3}{7} + \frac{4}{7} = \frac{7}{7} = 1$.

In the fraction $\frac{3}{7}$, the 3 is the **numerator** and 7 is the **denominator**.

$\frac{3}{7}$ is a **proper fraction** because its numerator is smaller than its denominator.

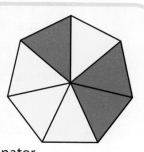

1   Look at these shapes.

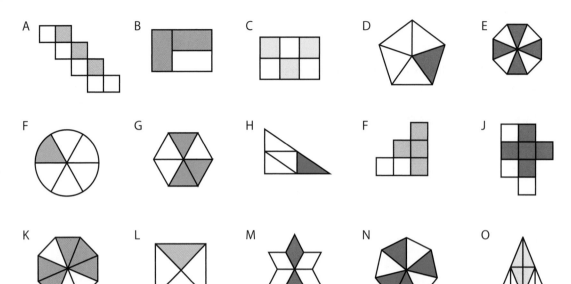

a   Which shape has $\frac{1}{5}$ shaded?

b   Which shape has $\frac{1}{6}$ shaded?

c   Which shape has $\frac{4}{7}$ shaded?

d   Which shape has $\frac{3}{8}$ shaded?

Name:

e   two shapes that have $\frac{1}{4}$ shaded.

f   three shapes that have $\frac{2}{3}$ shaded.

g   two shapes that have $\frac{5}{8}$ shaded.

h   four shapes that have $\frac{1}{2}$ shaded.

2   Look at the compass directions.

a   What fraction of a turn takes you from facing W to facing E?

b   How many half turns take you from facing S to facing S again?

c   What fraction of a clockwise turn takes you from facing N to facing W?

d   How many quarter turns take you from facing N to facing N again?

e   What fraction of a clockwise turn takes you from facing S to facing SW?

f   What fraction of a clockwise turn takes you from facing N to facing NW?

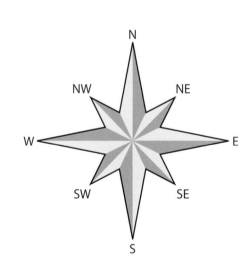

3 Copy and complete these statements.

a $\frac{1}{12} + \frac{11}{12} = \square$

b $1 - \frac{2}{3} = \square$

c $\frac{4}{7} + \square = 1$

d $1 - \frac{5}{11} = \square$

e $\frac{1}{4} + 2\frac{3}{4} = \square$

f $\square + \frac{2}{9} = 1$

4 a Amy drinks two thirds of a bottle of milk. What fraction is left?

b Asif spent $\frac{5}{8}$ of his pocket money. What fraction does he have left?

c John has a bag of sugar. He uses $\frac{3}{10}$ of the sugar to make a cake. What fraction of the sugar is left?

d Hannah has saved $\frac{5}{9}$ of the cost of a bike. What fraction of the cost does she still need to save?

5 Use the fraction wall. Which fraction is greater?

a $\frac{1}{6}$ or $\frac{1}{5}$

b $\frac{2}{7}$ or $\frac{2}{5}$

c $\frac{2}{7}$ or $\frac{1}{5}$

d $\frac{5}{8}$ or $\frac{4}{7}$

e $\frac{3}{4}$ or $\frac{5}{6}$

f $\frac{3}{8}$ or $\frac{2}{5}$

| $\frac{1}{8}$ | $\frac{1}{8}$ | $\frac{1}{8}$ | $\frac{1}{8}$ | $\frac{1}{8}$ | $\frac{1}{8}$ | $\frac{1}{8}$ | $\frac{1}{8}$ |

| $\frac{1}{7}$ | $\frac{1}{7}$ | $\frac{1}{7}$ | $\frac{1}{7}$ | $\frac{1}{7}$ | $\frac{1}{7}$ | $\frac{1}{7}$ |

| $\frac{1}{6}$ | $\frac{1}{6}$ | $\frac{1}{6}$ | $\frac{1}{6}$ | $\frac{1}{6}$ | $\frac{1}{6}$ |

| $\frac{1}{5}$ | $\frac{1}{5}$ | $\frac{1}{5}$ | $\frac{1}{5}$ | $\frac{1}{5}$ |

| $\frac{1}{4}$ | $\frac{1}{4}$ | $\frac{1}{4}$ | $\frac{1}{4}$ |

Points to remember

⊙ A fraction of a shape and the fraction that is left make up one whole.
For example:
if $\frac{3}{8}$ of a shape is shaded, then $\frac{5}{8}$ is not shaded;
if $\frac{2}{5}$ of a class are girls, then $\frac{3}{5}$ are boys.

⊙ Some fractions can be written more simply. For example:
$\frac{5}{10}, \frac{4}{8}, \frac{3}{6}$ are all the same as $\frac{1}{2}$; $\frac{3}{12}$ and $\frac{2}{8}$ are the same as $\frac{1}{4}$.

2 Equivalent fractions

This lesson will help you to identify equivalent fractions.

To find an **equivalent fraction**, multiply or divide the numerator and denominator by the same number.

Example 1 $\quad \frac{3}{5} = \frac{3 \times 4}{5 \times 4} = \frac{12}{20}$

To **simplify** or **cancel** a fraction, divide the numerator and denominator by the same number.

Example 2 $\quad \frac{12}{20} = \frac{^{3}\cancel{12}}{_{5}\cancel{20}} = \frac{3}{5}$

An **improper fraction** has a numerator that is bigger than the denominator, e.g. $\frac{8}{3}$.

A **mixed number** has a whole-number part and a fraction part, e.g. $5\frac{2}{3}$.

Exercise 2

1. Copy and complete these equivalent fractions.

   a $\frac{2}{3} = \frac{\square}{9}$
   b $\frac{5}{8} = \frac{\square}{24}$
   c $\frac{2}{11} = \frac{14}{\square}$
   d $\frac{9}{2} = \frac{27}{\square}$

   e $\frac{7}{20} = \frac{\square}{100}$
   f $\frac{8}{5} = \frac{\square}{15}$
   g $\frac{5}{9} = \frac{20}{\square}$
   h $\frac{12}{5} = \frac{144}{\square}$

2. Cancel each of these fractions to its simplest form.

   a $\frac{4}{12}$
   b $\frac{15}{25}$
   c $\frac{16}{24}$
   d $\frac{25}{35}$
   e $\frac{50}{20}$
   f $\frac{120}{10}$

3. What fraction is each of these? Write each fraction in its simplest form.

   a 6 out of 14
   b 18 out of 27
   c £10 out of £45
   d 300 g out of 500 g
   e 250 m out of 750 m
   f 60° out of 360°

4. Clocks have 12 divisions around the clock face.

   What fraction of a whole turn does the minute hand make between these times?

   Write each fraction in its simplest form.

   a 10:15 and 10:45 am
   b 2:15 and 2:35 pm

   c 5:20 and 5:30
   d 4:25 and 4:40

   e 3:05 and 3:30
   f 7:00 and 7:45

5 **a** What fraction of 3 hours is 15 minutes?

b What fraction of 1 litre is 50 millilitres?

 6 There are 360° in one whole turn.
What fraction of the whole circle is each of these sectors?
Write each fraction in its simplest form.

a
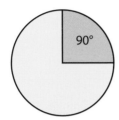

b
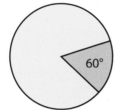

c
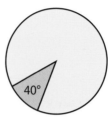

d
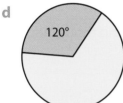

e
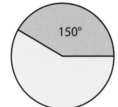

f
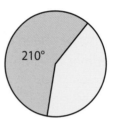

Extension problem

 7 Use eight of the numbers 1 to 10.

Use each number only once, so two numbers will not be used.

Make a pair of equivalent fractions.

Now make a different pair of equivalent fractions.

Now use the numbers 1 to 20.
How many pairs of equivalent fractions can you make?
Which numbers are not used? Why?

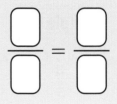

Points to remember

⊙ To **simplify** or **cancel** a fraction, divide the numerator and denominator by the same number.

⊙ To find an **equivalent fraction**, multiply or divide the numerator and denominator by the same number.

⊙ An **improper fraction** has a numerator that is bigger than the denominator.

⊙ A **mixed number** has a whole-number part and a fraction part.

3 Changing fractions to decimals

This lesson will help you to change fractions to decimals and vice versa.

You can write a decimal as a fraction by looking at its parts.

Example 1 $3.9 = 3 + 0.9 = 3 + \frac{9}{10} = 3\frac{9}{10}$

Example 2 $1.71 = 1 + 0.71 = 1 + \frac{71}{100} = 1\frac{71}{100}$

Example 3 $6.247 = 6 + 0.247 = 6 + \frac{247}{1000} = 6\frac{247}{1000}$

After a decimal has been expressed as a number of tenths, hundredths and thousandths, it can sometimes be simplified by cancelling. For example:

$0.32 = \frac{32}{100} = \frac{8}{25}$, cancelling by 4

$0.05 = \frac{5}{100} = \frac{1}{20}$, cancelling by 5

You can change a fraction to a decimal using your calculator.

Example 4   Change $\frac{3}{8}$ to a decimal.

$\frac{3}{8}$ means $3 \div 8$, so divide 3 by 8 on your calculator.

 0.375

Sometimes when you change a fraction to a decimal the digits repeat themselves. We call these **recurring decimals**.
For example, $0.\dot{3}$ (nought point three recurring) is shorthand for 0.333333333… or $\frac{1}{3}$.

Exercise 3

1. Write each decimal as a fraction in its simplest form.

   a 0.7   b 0.27   c 0.813   d 0.6   e 0.35   f 0.625

2. Write each decimal as a mixed number.

   a 1.25   b 6.4   c 7.125   d 3.6   e 4.05   f 20.003

3. **Use your calculator** to change each fraction to a decimal.

   a $\frac{3}{10}$ b $\frac{53}{100}$ c $\frac{427}{1000}$ d $\frac{5}{8}$ e $\frac{9}{25}$ f $\frac{7}{200}$

4 **Use your calculator** to change each improper fraction to a decimal.

   a $\frac{7}{5}$ b $\frac{25}{8}$ c $\frac{266}{50}$ d $\frac{33}{25}$ e $\frac{21}{2}$ f $\frac{163}{40}$

5 Work with a partner.

In each problem, use all four digits, putting one digit in each box.

Make a fraction and its decimal equivalent.

The fraction may be a proper fraction or an improper fraction.

  a Use all the digits 1, 2, 4 and 5.   b Use all the digits 1, 2, 3 and 5.

$$\frac{\Box}{\Box} = 0.\Box\Box \qquad\qquad \frac{\Box}{\Box} = \Box.\Box$$

  c Use all the digits 5, 6, 7 and 8.   d Use all the digits 2, 3, 5 and 7.

$$\frac{\Box}{\Box} = 0.\Box\Box \qquad\qquad \frac{\Box}{\Box} = \Box.\Box$$

Extension problem

6 **Use your calculator** to investigate these.

  a A fraction with a numerator of 1 and a denominator less than 50 is turned into a decimal using a calculator. The calculator display shows:

     0.033333333

    What was the fraction?

  b Another fraction with a numerator of 1 and a denominator less than 50 is turned into a decimal. This time the display shows:

     0.022222222

    What was the fraction?

⦿ Points to remember

- ⊙ To change a fraction to a decimal, divide the numerator by the denominator. You can use a calculator to do this.
- ⊙ To change a decimal to a fraction, consider the tenths, hundredths and thousandths, e.g.

$$0.627 = 0.6 + 0.02 + 0.007$$
$$0.627 = \frac{6}{10} + \frac{2}{100} + \frac{7}{1000} = \frac{627}{1000}$$

- ⊙ Equivalent fractions are represented by the same decimal number.

4 Equivalent fractions, decimals and percentages

This lesson will help you to identify equivalent fractions, decimals and percentages.

Percentage means 'per hundred', or 'in every hundred'. 35% is equivalent to $\frac{35}{100}$.

It is easy to change a percentage to a decimal.

Example 1   Write 47% as a decimal.

47% means $\frac{47}{100} = 0.47$.

Example 2   Write 125% as a decimal.

125% means $\frac{125}{100} = 1\frac{25}{100} = 1.25$.

To change a decimal to a percentage, multiply it by 100.

Example 3   Write 0.76 as a percentage.

$0.76 \times 100 = 76$, so 0.76 is equivalent to 76%.

Example 4   Write 1.23 as a percentage.

$1.23 \times 100 = 123$, so 1.23 is equivalent to 123%.

To change a percentage to a fraction, write it as a fraction with a denominator of 100. Simplify the fraction if you can.

Example 5   Write 25% as a fraction.

25% is $\frac{25}{100}$, which simplifies to $\frac{1}{4}$.

To change a fraction to a percentage, change it to a decimal, then multiply it by 100.

Example 6   Write $\frac{3}{10}$ as a percentage.

$\frac{3}{10}$ is $0.3 \times 100\% = 30\%$.

Exercise 4

1 Change these decimals to percentages.

    a 0.57   b 0.3   c 0.05   d 0.375   e 1.25   f 9.7

2 Change these percentages to decimals.

    a 35%   b 48%   c 2%   d 110%   e 18%   f 12.5%

3. Change these percentages to fractions. Write each fraction in its simplest form.

   a 70%   b 42%   c 5%   d 125%   e 31%   f 18%

4. Change these fractions to percentages.

   a $\frac{4}{5}$ b $\frac{2}{25}$ c $\frac{23}{50}$ d $\frac{11}{20}$ e $1\frac{3}{4}$ f $\frac{1}{8}$

5. Solve these problems.

   a 100 people were asked if they downloaded podcasts.
      52 of them said yes.
      What percentage of the people downloaded podcasts?

   b In a group of 20 teenagers, 4 of them did not have a
      mobile phone. What percentage of the teenagers
      had no mobile phone?

   c Ruth did a survey of 200 people.
      50 of them were left-handed.
      What percentage of the people were left-handed?

   d 50 children attend a playgroup.
      31 of them are boys.
      What percentage are girls?

   e Mark asked 60 people to name their favourite fruit.
      20 of them said strawberries.
      What percentage of the people said strawberries?

 Points to remember

   ⊙ **Percentage** means 'per hundred', or 'in every hundred'.
      Percentages like 47% can be written as $\frac{47}{100}$ or as 0.47.
   ⊙ To change a decimal or a fraction to a percentage, multiply it by 100

5 Adding and subtracting simple fractions

This lesson will help you to add and subtract simple fractions and solve problems.

When you add or subtract fractions, you must make the denominators the same.
To do this, find the lowest common multiple of the two denominators.

Example 1   Work out $\frac{1}{3} + \frac{1}{4}$.

The lowest common multiple of 3 and 4 is 12, so change both fractions to twelfths.

$$\frac{1}{3} + \frac{1}{4} = \frac{4}{12} + \frac{3}{12} = \frac{7}{12}$$

The numerator of the answer is the sum of the numerators of the two fractions.
The denominator does not change.

Sometimes you can cancel the answer to its simplest form.

Example 2 $\frac{5}{12} - \frac{1}{6} = \frac{5}{12} - \frac{2}{12} = \frac{3}{12} = \frac{1}{4}$

Exercise 5

① Work out each of these. Where necessary, change the answer to a mixed number.
Write each answer in its simplest form.

a $\frac{1}{3} + \frac{1}{4}$ b $\frac{1}{6} + \frac{1}{9}$ c $\frac{3}{10} + \frac{1}{4}$

d $\frac{1}{8} + \frac{5}{6}$ e $\frac{4}{5} + \frac{3}{10}$ f $\frac{2}{3} + \frac{1}{6} + \frac{1}{4}$

② Here are some number cards.

Make fractions using one card for the numerator and one
for the denominator.

a How many different fractions less than $\frac{1}{2}$ can you make?
Write each of the possible fractions.

b For each of your fractions, how much less than 1 is it?

③ Work out each of these. Write each answer in its simplest form.

a $\frac{1}{3} - \frac{1}{4}$ b $\frac{5}{6} - \frac{1}{3}$ c $\frac{7}{10} - \frac{1}{4}$

d $\frac{4}{5} - \frac{3}{10}$ e $\frac{7}{8} - \frac{5}{6}$ f $\frac{3}{4} + \frac{1}{3} - \frac{1}{2}$

4 Solve these problems. Show your working.

a How much more is two thirds of a litre than one sixth of a litre?

b In a magazine there are two adverts on the same page.
The first advert uses one quarter of the page.
The second advert uses one eighth of the page.

What fraction of the whole page do the two adverts use?

c One half of the passengers on a flight to Holland are British.
Three eighths are Dutch.
The rest are other nationalities.

What fraction of all the passengers are other nationalities?

d Tammy and Sean are teenagers.
The difference between one sixth of Tammy's age in years and one seventh of Sean's age in years is one year.

How old is Tammy? How old is Sean?

Extension problem

 Did you know that...?

Brahmagupta (598 to 668) was the most important Indian mathematician of his time. He is said to have invented the idea of zero.

He was also a clever astronomer. He worked out how to calculate when the planets would rise and set in the sky and when eclipses of the Sun and Moon would happen.

5 This problem is based on one written 1400 years ago by Brahmagupta.

Brahma had some apples in a tub.
He gave one third of the apples to Rupa.
He gave one quarter of the apples to Bashir.
He gave one fifth of the apples to Gita.
He kept 13 apples for himself.

How many apples were in the tub?

6 Fractions of whole-number quantities

This lesson will help you to multiply a fraction by a whole number and to solve problems involving working out fractions of numbers, money and measures.

$\frac{2}{3} \times 4$ means $\frac{2}{3} + \frac{2}{3} + \frac{2}{3} + \frac{2}{3}$.

The diagrams below show that $\frac{2}{3} + \frac{2}{3} + \frac{2}{3} + \frac{2}{3}$ is $\frac{8}{3}$ or $2\frac{2}{3}$.

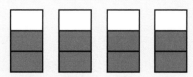 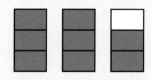

You can work out $\frac{2}{3} \times 4$ without referring to diagrams. The calculation is $\frac{2 \times 4}{3} = \frac{8}{3} = 2\frac{2}{3}$.

Exercise 6

1. Work out these calculations. Where necessary, change the answer to a mixed number. Write each fraction in its simplest form.

   a $\frac{3}{8} \times 2$ b $6 \times \frac{4}{5}$

   c $\frac{9}{10} \times 3$ d $\frac{3}{4} \times 8$

   e $4 \times \frac{7}{12}$ f $\frac{3}{7} \times 5$

   g $6 \times \frac{2}{9}$ h $\frac{7}{11} \times 22$

2. Work out these calculations.

   a $\frac{2}{3}$ of 66   b $\frac{3}{4}$ of 48   c $\frac{4}{5}$ of 65

   d $\frac{3}{10}$ of £150   e $\frac{2}{5}$ of 80 litres   f $\frac{3}{8}$ of 72 miles

   g $\frac{5}{9}$ of 54 minutes   h $\frac{7}{10}$ of 80 seconds   i $\frac{4}{7}$ of 28 days

3 Solve these problems. Show your working.

a Rakesh needs £80 to buy a bike.
He has saved one quarter of this.
His father has given him half of the rest.
How much money does Rakesh still need?

b One lap of a cycle track is $\frac{3}{4}$ of a mile.
John rode 7 laps on his bike.
How far did he ride?

c Sarah spent three fifths of her savings of £100.
How much money did she spend?

d Leena fills each of 5 cups with two fifths of a litre of lemonade.
How much lemonade does she use?

e A new pair of trainers costs £39.
Billy's uncle has given him two thirds of the money.
How much has Billy been given?

f Josh put three tenths of a kilogram of strawberries in each of 6 boxes.
What is the total weight of the strawberries that Josh put in the boxes?

g Two fifths of the 250 pupils in a school wear glasses.
How many of the pupils do not wear glasses?

h Mary and Alison painted the Youth Club.
Mary worked for 6 hours. Alison worked for 2 hours.
They got paid £40 for the whole job.
What fraction of the work did Mary do?
How much should she get paid?

Points to remember

⊙ To find $\frac{1}{8}$, divide by 8.

⊙ To find $\frac{3}{8}$, find $\frac{1}{8}$ and multiply it by 3.

⊙ To find $\frac{1}{4}$, find one half of one half.

⊙ To find $\frac{3}{4}$, work out $\frac{1}{4}$ then multiply it by 3.

7 Percentages of whole-number quantities

This lesson will help you to work out percentages of whole numbers and to solve percentage problems involving numbers, money or measures.

To find 50% of a number or quantity, halve it.
To find 25%, find half of 50%.
To find 75%, add 50% and 25%.

To find 10%, divide the number or quantity by 10.
To find 5%, find 10%, and then halve it.
To find 15%, find 10%, then add 5%.

If there is no quick method for finding a percentage of a quantity, first find 1%, then multiply by the value of the percentage. Use your calculator where appropriate.

Example   Find 13% of £25.

1% of £25 is £25 ÷ 100 = £0.25
13% of £25 is £0.25 × 13 = £3.25

To work out this calculation with a calculator, press these keys.

Exercise 7

1   Use estimation to match each percentage calculation to its answer. For example:

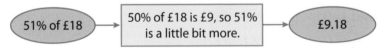

51% of £18 → 50% of £18 is £9, so 51% is a little bit more. → £9.18

Now match these pairs.

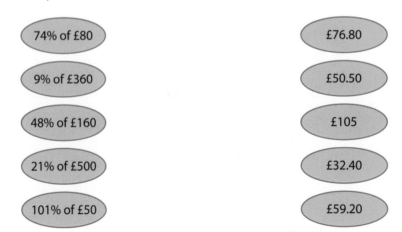

74% of £80		£76.80
9% of £360		£50.50
48% of £160		£105
21% of £500		£32.40
101% of £50		£59.20

(2) **Without using your calculator**, work out the answers to these calculations.

a   50% of £250
b   25% of 300 kg
c   75% of 440 cm

d   10% of 72 g
e   5% of 200 litres
f   15% of £600

g   20% of 500
h   60% of 200 m

(3) **Use a calculator** to work out the answers to these calculations.

a   35% of 460
b   48% of £600
c   41% of 32 kg

d   5% of 75 m
e   30% of 360°
f   45% of 320 litres

g   76% of £280
h   55% of 3 hours

(4) Solve these problems. **Use your calculator** when appropriate.

a   Three quarters of the pupils in a school have at least one dental filling.

What percentage of the pupils have no dental fillings?

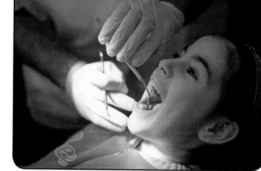

b   David counted 50 cars in the school car park.
28% of them were silver.
How many cars were silver?
What percentage of the cars were not silver?

c   There are 25 pupils in a class. 64% of them are girls.
How many pupils are girls?
What percentage of the class are boys?

d   80% of the pupils in a school walk to school.
What fraction do not walk to school?

e   A savings account pays 9% interest each year.
Wendy put £50 into her account.
How much interest does she get after one year?

f   Four friends had dinner in a restaurant. The total bill was £60.
The friends added a tip of 15% of the total.
How much did they pay altogether?

⊙ **Points to remember**

⊙ To find 20% of a quantity, find 10% by dividing by 10, then multiply by 2 to find 20%. You can find 30%, 40%, 50%, … similarly.

⊙ If there is no quick method for finding a percentage of a quantity, find 1%, then multiply by the value of the percentage.

⊙ Include any units in the answer.

How well are you doing?

Fractions and percentages (no calculator)

1. 10% of a number is 21. What is the number?

2. Write 80% as a fraction.

3. What fraction of this shape is shaded?

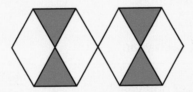

   Write your fraction as simply as possible.

4. Which of these is less than one half?

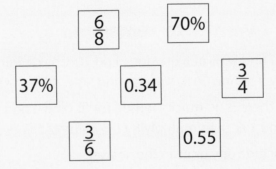

5. Work out 45% of £400.

(6) James had £75. He gave £60 to his sister.
What percentage of his money did James give to his sister?

(7) Kelly can swim one length of the pool in $\frac{2}{3}$ of a minute.
How long does she take to swim 15 lengths of the pool?

(8) This chart shows the results of a survey.

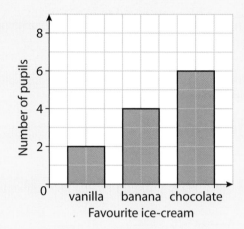

All the pupils in a class said which ice-cream they like best.
Each of them chose one kind of ice-cream.
How many pupils are in the class?
What percentage of the class likes chocolate ice-cream best?

(9) There are some coloured cubes in a box.
Three quarters of the cubes are blue.
One sixth of the cubes are green.
The rest of the cubes are red.
What fraction of the cubes are red?

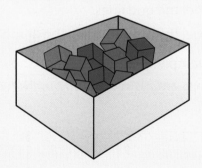

Grouped data and simple statistics

This unit will help you to:

- draw diagrams and graphs to represent data;
- interpret pie charts;
- find averages and the range for sets of data;
- say what diagrams, graphs and statistics tell you.

1 Constructing charts and tables

This lesson will help you to draw graphs and find the modal class for grouped data.

Bar-line graphs

A **bar-line graph** is used to display numerical data that can only take certain values.

- A bar-line graph is like a bar chart with very thin bars.
- Evenly space the bar-lines on the horizontal axis.
- Put 'Frequency' on the vertical axis. Label the grid lines.
- Label the axes and give the graph a title.

For example this bar-line graph shows the numbers of brothers and sisters for the pupils in a class.

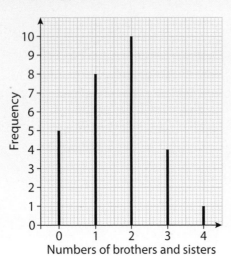

Work in a group of four. You will need a copy of **S3.1 Resource sheet 1.1** per group, and a pencil, ruler and coloured pen.

The table below shows how many times each numbered ball has come up in the National Lottery (data from www.national-lottery.co.uk).

Ball number	Frequency		Ball number	Frequency		Ball number	Frequency
1	14		18	10		34	18
2	14		19	13		35	15
3	13		20	12		36	15
4	15		21	14		37	13
5	10		22	17		38	14
6	15		23	22		39	15
7	21		24	12		40	14
8	15		25	19		41	14
9	15		26	18		42	21
10	11		27	13		43	18
11	16		28	11		44	16
12	13		29	19		45	18
13	16		30	22		46	12
14	19		31	16		47	18
15	13		32	12		48	17
16	9		33	11		49	14
17	13						

Your teacher will tell you which ball numbers to use.
Use a ruler to help you to find the data on the table.

a Label the marks on the horizontal axis on Resource sheet 1.1 with your set of ball numbers.

b Find out how many times each of your ball numbers has come up in the National Lottery.

c Use a pencil and a ruler to draw a bar-line to show the frequency for each of your ball numbers.

d When you are sure that your bar-lines are correct, go over them using a coloured pen and a ruler.

Discrete data and frequency diagrams

Discrete data can only take certain values. You can't, for example, have a fractional number of brothers and sisters. The number has to be a whole number.

When you draw a **frequency diagram** for grouped discrete data, all the bars should be the same width. The gaps between the bars should be the same width as well.

For example, this frequency diagram shows some test scores.

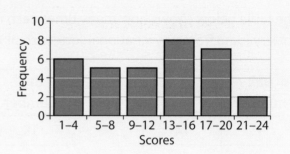

Exercise 1B

You will need squared paper.

1. The table shows the number of pupils of different ages in a table-tennis club.
   Draw a bar-line graph for the data.

Age	11	12	13	14	15
Frequency	12	10	7	9	4

   Use a vertical frequency scale numbered in 1s.
   Space the bar-lines at 2 cm intervals horizontally.

2. The table shows the mental mathematics test scores for a class.
   Draw a bar-line graph for the data.

Score	4	5	6	7	8	9	10
Frequency	2	3	3	5	4	2	4

   Use a vertical frequency scale numbered in 1s.
   Space the bar-lines at 2 cm intervals horizontally.

3. In a test the marks are given as percentages.
   The data has been grouped into the table below. Draw a frequency diagram for the data.

Mark (%)	1–10	11–20	21–30	31–40	41–50	51–60	61–70	71–80	81–90	91–100
Frequency	2	4	1	7	5	9	5	7	4	3

   Use a vertical frequency scale numbered in 1s.
   Space the bars at 1 cm intervals horizontally. Make the bars 1 cm wide.

4	All the pupils in Year 8 in a school wrote a story.

The number of spelling mistakes each pupil made was recorded.

The data was grouped into the table below. Draw a frequency diagram for the data.

Number of spelling mistakes	1–5	6–10	11–15	16–20	21–25	26–30
Frequency	6	8	9	16	8	3

Use a vertical frequency scale numbered in 2s.

Space the bars at 1 cm intervals horizontally. Make the bars 1 cm wide.

Points to remember

- Leave equal spaces between the bars or lines on a graph.
- Label lines, not spaces, on the frequency axis.
- Groups of data should not overlap.
- The modal class is the group that occurs most often.

2 Calculating statistics

This lesson will help you to find the mode, median, mean and range for small sets of data.

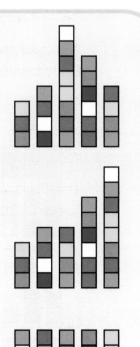

These five towers are made from cubes.

The towers have 3, 4, 8, 6 and 4 cubes in them.

Arrange the towers in order of height.

Put all the towers of the same height next to each other.

The most common height is 4.

This is called the **mode** for the heights.

The middle height is 4.

This is called the **median** height.

Make all the towers the same height. There are 5 cubes in each tower.

This is called the **mean** of the heights.

You can work out the mean like this:

    Total number of cubes ÷ number of towers

The mode, median and mean are different ways of finding the average of a set of numbers.

- The **mode** is the number that occurs most often in the set.
- The **mean** is found by adding up all the numbers in the set and dividing by the number of numbers in the set.
- The **median** is the middle number, or the mean of the middle two numbers, when all the numbers in the set are arranged in order.
- The **range** is the difference between the largest and smallest numbers in the set. It is a measure of how spread out the numbers are.

Example

Ten pupils took a spelling test and got these scores: 3, 8, 5, 9, 10, 4, 7, 8, 4, 8.
Find the mean, median, mode and range.

The **mean** is (3 + 8 + 5 + 9 + 10 + 4 + 7 + 8 + 4 + 8) ÷ 10 = 66 ÷ 10 = 6.6.

The scores in order are 3, 4, 4, 5, 7, 8, 8, 8, 9, 10.
The two middle numbers are 7 and 8 so the **median** is 7.5.

The **mode** is 8.

The **range** is 10 − 3 = 7.

Exercise 2

1. Work with a partner. You will need some interlocking cubes.
   Find the mean, median, mode and range for the heights of the towers in each set.

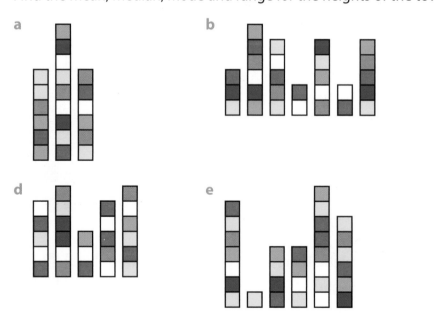

a   b   c

d   e

② There are six classes in an infant school.

The numbers of pupils in each class are 26, 25, 28, 24, 22 and 25.

a What is the mean number of pupils in a class?

b What is the range?

③ In a club there are twelve members.

Their ages are 13, 11, 12, 14, 13, 12, 11, 14, 12, 12, 13, 11.

a What is the mean age of the members
in the club?

b What is the range of their ages?

c What is the mode?

d What is the median age?

e What do you notice about the
mean, median and mode?

④ In a mental arithmetic test, ten pupils got these scores:
9, 6, 4, 8, 7, 9, 10, 5, 8, 9.

a What is the mean score?

b What is the range of their scores?

c What is the mode?

d What is the median score?

e What do you notice about the mode as a measure of the average score?
Why do you think that this has happened?

⑤ Mrs Phipps keeps a record of the number of tomatoes
she picks off her tomato plants each week.

The table shows her records.

Week	1	2	3	4	5	6
Number of tomatoes	7	12	11	9	13	8

a What is the mean number of tomatoes?

b What is the range?

c What is the mode?

d What is the median?

6 Mrs Phipps also grows pumpkins and records their mass. The masses of the pumpkins are:

| 2.4 kg | 1.8 kg | 0.9 kg | 2.1 kg |
| 1.5 kg | 1.7 kg | 2.2 kg | 1.1 kg |

a What is the mean mass of the pumpkins?

b What is the range?

c What is the median?

Extension problem

7 You will need a dice.

a Roll the dice ten times to get a set of ten numbers. Write down the ten numbers.

Work out the mean, median, mode and range of your set of ten numbers.

b Roll the dice ten more times to get another set of ten numbers.

Work out the mean, median, mode and range of your second set of ten numbers.

c What is the smallest range you can get with ten numbers from a dice? What numbers will you need to roll on the dice get this range?

⊙ Points to remember

⊙ An **average** is a number that represents all the numbers in a set.
  - The **mode** is the number that occurs most often in the set.
  - To find the **mean**, add up all the numbers in the set and divide by the number of numbers in the set.
  - The **median** is the middle number, or the mean of the middle two numbers, when you put all the numbers in the set in order.

⊙ The **range** is the difference between the largest and smallest numbers in a set.

3 Interpreting graphs and diagrams

This lesson will help you to interpret diagrams and graphs and say something about what the shape of the graph tells you.

Different types of graph are used for different types of data and show different information.

For example, a **pie chart** is good for showing the proportions of each category.

Example 1

The pie chart is about the number of brothers and sisters for the pupils in a class.

What does the graph tell you?

The chart shows that more people had two brothers or sisters than any other number.

Fewer people had only one brother or sister.

Very few people had four or more brothers and sisters.

About three times as many people had three brothers and sisters than had four or more.

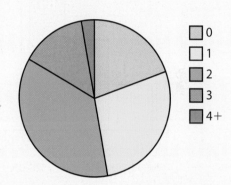

Bar-line graphs, bar charts and frequency diagrams show the frequency of each category or group. They also show the total frequency of all the data.

Example 2

The bar-line graph is about the number of brothers or sisters for the pupils in a class.

What does the graph show?

The graph shows that the most common number of brothers and sisters is two.

There are more pupils with zero or one brothers and sisters than there are with two.

Only one person in the class has four or more brothers or sisters, but five people had no brothers or sisters.

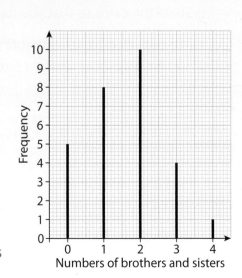

Grouped frequency diagrams are used for data that is grouped together.

Example 3

20 pupils took a maths test.
Their test marks are shown on the right.

Draw a frequency diagram to show the data.

Solution

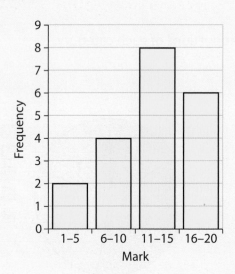

Mark	Tally	Frequency
1–5	II	2
6–10	IIII	4
11–15	IIII III	8
16–20	IIII I	6

Exercise 3A

① Work in a group of four. You will need a copy of the cards from **S3.1 Resource sheet 3.1**. The data on the cards is from www.nationmaster.com.

Share the cards so that you have two each. Keep them secret from others in your group.

Pair the cards by asking other pupils questions.
You mustn't show them a card until you are sure that you have found a pair.

All the cards have a chart, diagram or table on them.
A pair of cards represents the same set of data.

Take turns to ask a question.

Here are some good questions to ask:

◉ Who has a chart or diagram with five categories of data on it?

◉ Who has a table with a quarter of the data in the same category?

When you have paired all the cards, write a sentence about what your pair of cards shows about the data.

1   The bar-line graph shows the number of
    people of different ages in a youth club.

    The club is for 11- to 16-year-olds.

    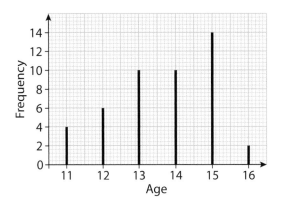

    a What is the most common age for young
       people in the club?

    b Write a sentence to say what the graph
       shows about the ages of the people in
       the club.

2   The pie chart shows the mental mathematics
    grades for pupils in a class.

    a Write a sentence to say what the pie chart shows.

    b Which grade was given to the most pupils?

    c Roughly what percentage of pupils
       got an A grade?

    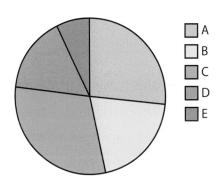

    d How many pupils got a C grade?

    e Trevor got a C grade.
       He thinks he is in the top half of the class.
       Is he right?

3   The grouped frequency diagram shows the marks some pupils got in a test.

    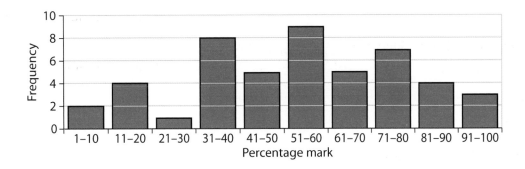

    a Which is the modal class (the group that happens most often)?

    b Do you think the test was too easy, too hard or about right?
       Explain your answer.

4   The graph shows how boys and girls travel to school.

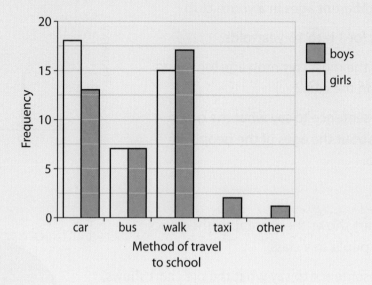

a   Which method of travel is most popular with boys?

b   Which method of travel is most popular with girls?

c   What are the similarities in the way boys and girls travel to school?

d   What are the differences?

 Points to remember

- A bar chart or bar-line graph shows:
  - the frequency of items in each category or group of data;
  - the total frequency of all the items of data.

  A pie chart does not show this information.

- Use a pie chart to show and compare the proportion of each category of data.

How well are you doing?

1. *2005 level 4*

   This question is about pupils in class 7Y.

   The graph shows how many of these pupils were at school each day.

   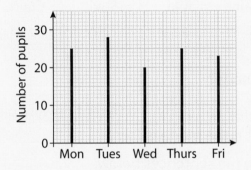

   a   On which days were only 25 pupils at school?

   b   On Tuesday all the pupils in class 7Y were at school.

      How many of these pupils were not at school on Wednesday?

2. A shop records the number of bottles of water sold each day for a month.

   The results are shown in the frequency diagram.

   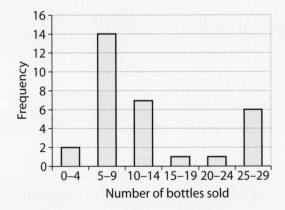

   a   On how many days were 15–19 bottles of water sold?

   b   What is the modal class for the number of bottles of water sold?

3 *2007 level 4*

Molly asked the pupils in her class
how many pets they had.
She recorded her results on a pie chart.

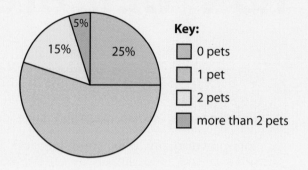

Key:
- 0 pets
- 1 pet
- 2 pets
- more than 2 pets

a What percentage of pupils had only
1 pet?

b There are 20 pupils in the class.
How many pupils had 0 pets?

4 *2007 level 4*

These are the names of the 12 people who work for a company.

Ali	Claire	Kiki	Suki	Claire	James
Brian	Claire	Lucy	Tom	Ryan	Tom

a What name is the mode?

b One person leaves the company. A different person joins the company.
Now the name that is the mode is Tom.

Copy and complete the sentences below.

The name of the person who leaves is ....

The name of the person who joins is ....

5 *2005 level 4*

a There are two children in the Smith family.
The range of their ages is exactly 7 years.

What could the ages of the two children be?
Give an example.

b There are two children in the Patel family.
They are twins of the same age.
What is the range of their ages?

Functional skills 1

School meals

This group activity will help you to:

- work out how to tackle an unfamiliar problem;
- choose and use the mathematics needed to solve it;
- communicate your findings;
- explain and justify your solution.

Background

School meals are a hot topic. There have even been TV programmes that investigated how they could be made healthier.

Here are some of the factors that have to be considered when menus for school meals are planned.

- What would pupils like to eat?
- What makes a healthy meal?
- How much will a meal cost?

Why are these factors important?

Background information

This is the average cost of the food for a typical school meal consisting of meat, potato and a vegetable, followed by a pudding.

meat	40p a portion
potato	£4 for 25 kg providing 100 portions
vegetable	£10 for 25 kg providing 100 portions
pudding	24p per portion

Maybury school canteen employs 12 staff.

The cook in charge earns £120 a week.

The rest earn £85 a week.

An average of 450 pupils have a school meal each day.

Problems

1 Fair price

What is a fair price for a school meal at Maybury school?

2 Pay rise

If all the staff at Maybury school get a 5% pay rise, by how much should the price of a meal increase?

3 Unpopular meals

If the number of pupils having a school meal falls to an average of 350 a day, how will this affect the price of a meal?

4 Your school

What are the labour costs and average number of meals served in your school?

Be prepared to justify your conclusions to other groups.

Angles

This unit will help you to:

- identify different types of angles;
- estimate and measure angles;
- label angles and lines correctly;
- know that the sum of angles on a straight line is 180° and at a point is 360°;
- recognise vertically opposite angles and know that they are equal.

1 Measuring and drawing angles

This lesson will help you to measure and draw angles accurately.

 Did you know that...?

Face of Big Ben

The London Eye

Tower Bridge

All these photographs show examples of **turning**. The amount of turn is called an **angle**.
The symbol ∠, meaning angle, was first used by a Frenchman, Pierre Hérigone, in 1634.

Here are examples of different **types of angles**.

Acute angle

Obtuse angle

Reflex angle

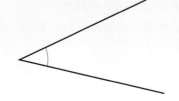

Measuring angles

When you measure angles, first estimate the size of the angle. Then use a protractor.

An estimate for the size of the angle is 40°.

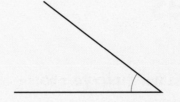

1   Place the centre of the protractor over the corner of the angle.

The base line of the protractor should be along one side of the angle.

2   Read the angle from 0° on the outer scale.

The angle is 37°.

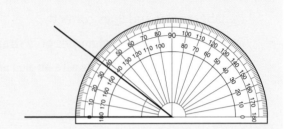

Drawing angles

1   To draw an angle of 54°, first draw a line segment.

2   Place the protractor on the line. The centre of the protractor must be at the end of the line segment.

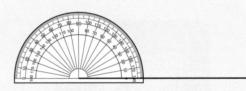

3   Mark off a point at 54°.

4   Join the end of the line to the point to make the angle. Mark the angle.

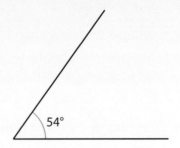

You will need a protractor.

1 Look at each angle.
Write whether it is **acute**, **obtuse**, or **reflex**.

a

b

c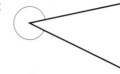

d

e

f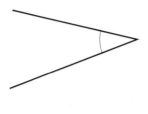

2 Estimate the size of each angle.

a

b

c

d

e

f

3 Use a protractor to measure these angles.

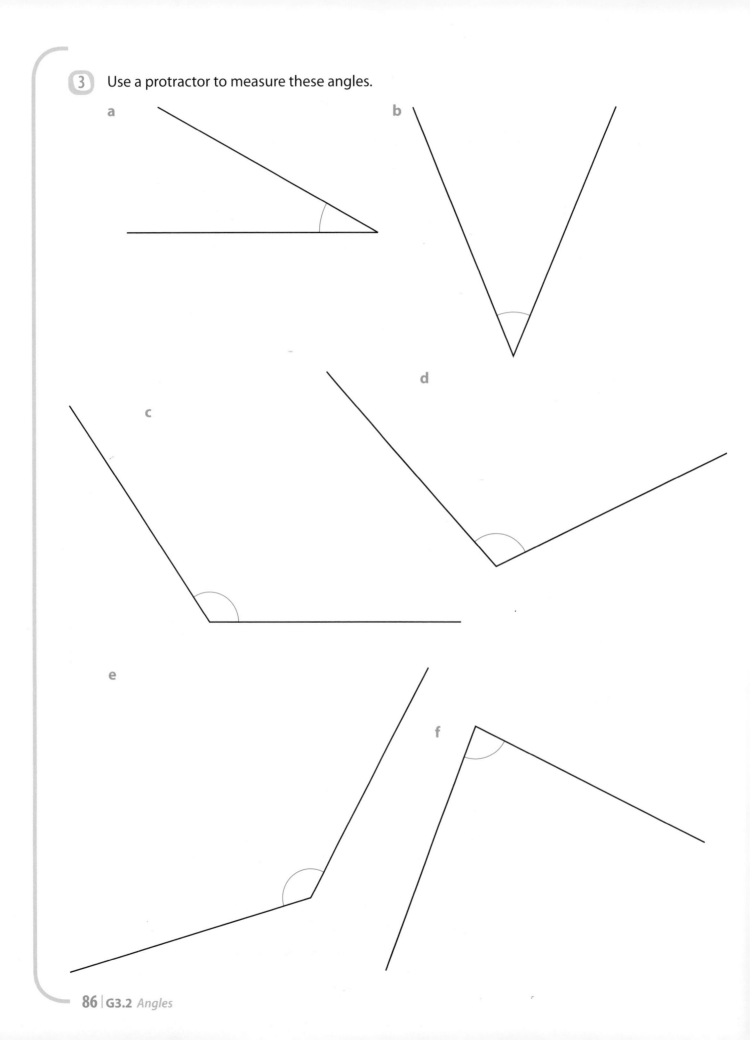

4 Use a protractor to draw these angles accurately.

a 70°   b 130°   c 49°   d 117°

5 For each clock, write down the size of the angle between the hands.

a

b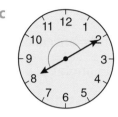

c

d

e

f

Extension problem

 a In 20 minutes, how many degrees does the minute hand of the clock turn?

b In 3 hours, how many degrees does the hour hand of the clock turn?

c The minute hand of a clock turns 180 degrees. How many degrees does the hour hand turn?

d How many times in 12 hours do the hands of a clock form a right angle?

○ **Points to remember**

⊙ An angle is a measure of **turn**. There are 360° in one whole turn.

⊙ An **acute angle** is between 0° and 90°.

⊙ An **obtuse angle** is between 90° and 180°.

⊙ An angle between 180° and 360° is a **reflex angle**.

⊙ When you measure or draw an angle:
 – first estimate its size, or decide if it is acute, obtuse or reflex;
 – line up the protractor correctly;
 – use the correct scale on the protractor.

2 Angles on a straight line

This lesson will help you to know that angles on a straight line add up to 180°.

Angles a, b and c are called **angles on a straight line**.

When you add angles a, b and c, you get 180°.

The angles on a straight line add up to 180°.

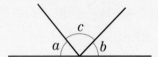

Exercise 2

You will need a protractor.

1   **a** Measure angles ACD and BCD.
        Work out their sum.

    b Measure angles
        PRS and QRS.
        Work out their sum.

   c Measure angles VXY, YXZ and WXZ.
        Work out their sum.

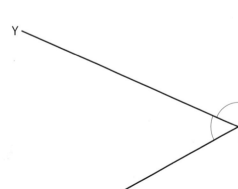

2 Calculate each angle marked with a letter.
Give your reasons.

a

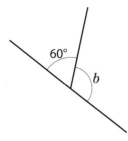

60°

b

b

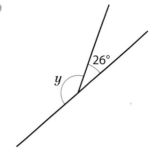

26°

y

c

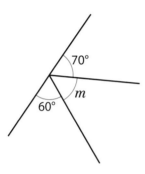

70°

m

60°

d

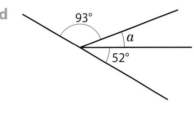

93°

a

52°

3 **a** Find angle ABC.

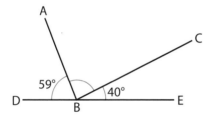

A

C

59°

40°

D

B

E

b Find angle ACE.

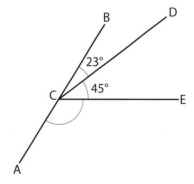

B

D

23°

45°

C

E

A

4 Find angles NRQ, QRM and MRP.

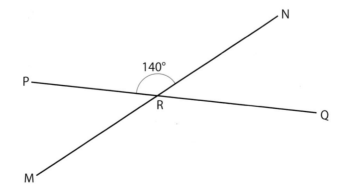

N

140°

P

R

Q

M

5 **a** Find the value of m.
Give a reason for your answer.

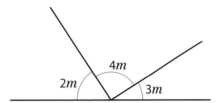

b Find the value of s.
Give a reason for your answer.

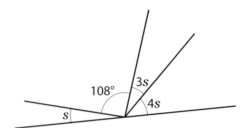

Extension problem

  Did you know that...?

Euclid was a famous mathematician of ancient times.

He is best known for the work he did on geometry.

No one knows much about his life.

We do know that he lived from about 325 BCE to 265 BCE. We also know that he was a teacher at Alexandria in Egypt.

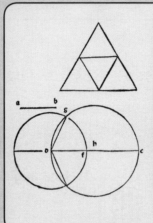

Euclid's work translated into Latin

6 How many times in 12 hours do the hands of a clock form a straight line?

 Points to remember

⊙ You can find an angle by measuring or calculating.
Check carefully to see if you should measure or calculate.

⊙ The sum of angles on a straight line is 180°.

3 Angles at a point

This lesson will help you to:

- know that angles at a point sum to 360°;
- recognise vertically opposite angles.

Angles a, b and c are called **angles at a point**.

When you add angles a, b and c, you get a full turn.

One full turn is the same as 360°.

The angles at a point add up to 360°.

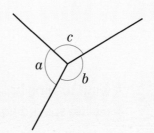

When two straight lines cross, opposite angles are equal.

$a = b$

The two unmarked angles are also equal to each other.

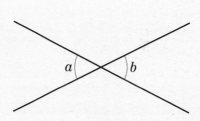

Exercise 3

1. Work out the size of each angle marked with a letter.
   Give reasons for your answers.

a

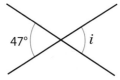

47° i

b

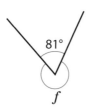

81°

f

c

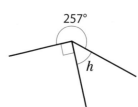

257°

h

d

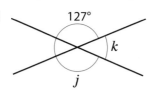

127°

k

j

e

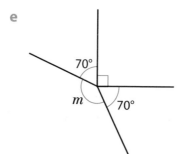

70°

m 70°

f

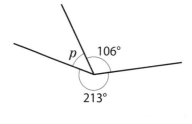

p 106°

213°

2 Find the size of each angle marked with a letter.
Explain your answers.

a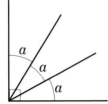

b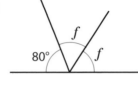

c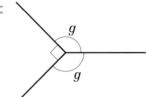

3 A wind turbine has 3 sails.
They are spaced equally.

What is the angle between each sail?

4 In the diagram, three straight lines meet at a point.

  a Find the value of x.

  b Find the value of y.

Give a reason for each answer.

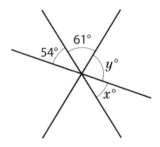

Extension problems

5 Calculate each angle marked with a letter.
Give reasons for your answers.

a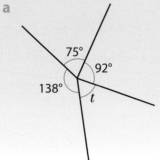

b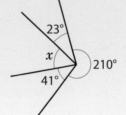

c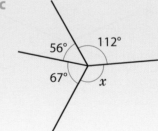

6 AB and CD are straight lines.

Angle AEC = 36°

Angle BEF = 73°

Work out the sizes of these angles.

Give your reasons.

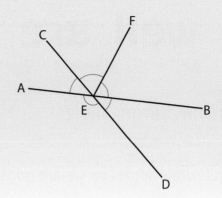

a Angle CEF

b Angle DEB

c Angle AED

 Points to remember

⊙ The sum of angles on a straight line is 180°.

⊙ The sum of angles at a point is 360°.

⊙ Vertically opposite angles are equal.

⊙ When you calculate angles, give your reasons.

How well are you doing?

Drawing and measuring angles

1   *2002 level 4*

Two pupils drew angles on square grids.

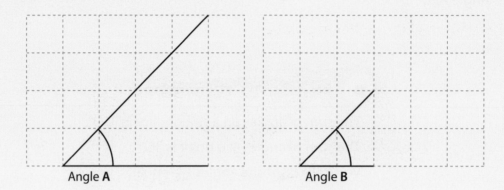

Angle **A**   Angle **B**

a   Which word below describes angle A?

   acute   obtuse   right-angled   reflex

   Write the correct word.

b   Is angle A bigger than angle B?
   Write **Yes** or **No**.
   Explain your answer.

2   Look at the triangle.

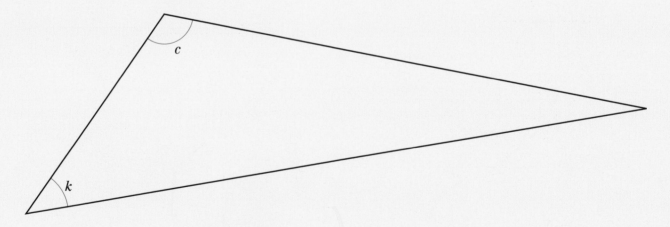

   a   Measure accurately angle k.

   b   Measure accurately angle c.

③ Use a ruler, protractor and sharp pencil.

    a Draw an angle of 55 degrees.

    b Draw an angle of 130 degrees.

Angles at a point, on a straight line and vertically opposite

④ *2007 level 5*

Three shapes fit together at point B.

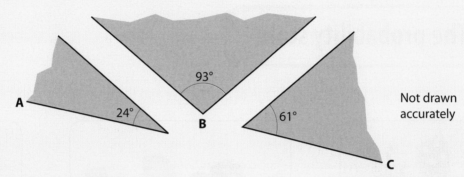

Not drawn
accurately

Will ABC make a straight line?
Write **Yes** or **No**.
Explain your answer.

⑤ Work out the size of each angle marked with a letter.
Give a reason for each answer.

a

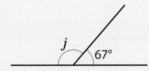

b

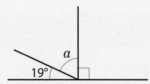

c

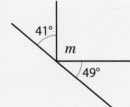

d

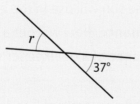

e

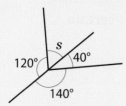

f

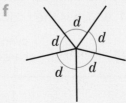

Probability 1

This unit will help you to:

- use words like 'certain', 'likely' or 'possible' to describe probability;
- use the probability scale of 0 to 1;
- work out probabilities of events.

1 The probability scale

This lesson will help you to use the language of probability and the probability scale.

Probability is the **likelihood** or **chance** of something happening.
You can describe probability using words such as

    impossible   **unlikely**   **even chance**   **likely**   **certain**

Here are some examples.

- It is **likely** that I will eat an apple today.
- It is **certain** that the sun will rise in the east tomorrow.
- There is an **even chance** that I will get a tail when I spin a fair coin.
- There is a **poor chance** of a goalkeeper scoring a hat trick.

Probability is measured on a scale of 0 to 1.

The **lowest** probability is **0**, which is the probability that something is **impossible**.
The **highest** probability is **1**, which is the probability that something is **certain**.

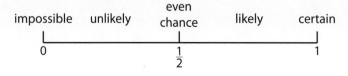

Exercise 1

1 Choose a probability word to complete each sentence in your book.

   a I am .... to pick a red counter from a bag full of red counters.

   b It is .... that I will be late for school tomorrow.

   c I am .... to get homework today.

   d It is .... I will see a fox on the way home from school.

   e I am .... to eat chips today.

2 Match one of these words each statement below. (You may use a word more than once.)

impossible very unlikely unlikely even chance likely very likely certain

   a It will snow in August in London.

   b I roll an ordinary dice and get an 8.

   c I will cross a road on my way home from school.

   d I will be first to leave the classroom at the end of the lesson.

   e I get exactly 100 heads when I toss a fair coin 200 times.

   f The first baby to be born on 1 January will be female.

3 The diagram shows a probability scale with five events, A, B, C, D and E.

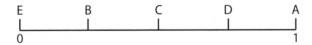

   a Which event is certain to occur?

   b Which event is impossible?

   c Which event is unlikely to occur but could happen?

   d What events are more likely to occur than event C?

   e What events are less likely to occur than event D?

④ Match the events below to the probabilities shown on this probability scale.

```
0   R   S   T       U           V   1
└───┴───┴───┴───────┴───────────┴───┘
```

a England will win the next World Cup.

b It will snow in Scotland in December.

c You will get a 6 when you roll a fair dice.

d You will get a head when you toss a fair coin.

e You will be late for school tomorrow.

⑤ Here are five spinners.

Spinner A   Spinner B   Spinner C   Spinner D   Spinner E

Each arrow is spun.

a On which spinner is the arrow **certain** to stop on red?

b On which spinner is the arrow **most likely** to stop on blue?

c On which spinner is the arrow **least likely** to stop on red?

d On which spinner is there an **even chance** that the arrow stops on red or blue?

⦿ **Points to remember**

⦿ Probability can be described using words such as

   impossible   unlikely   even chance   likely certain

   The word 'chance' is also used to describe probability.

⦿ Probability is measured on a scale from 0 (impossible) to 1 (certain).
   This can be shown on a probability scale.

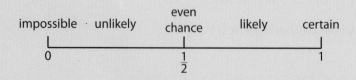

```
impossible · unlikely    even        likely      certain
                         chance
            └───────────────┴───────────────────┘
            0               1                    1
                            ─
                            2
```

2 Equally likely outcomes

This lesson will help you to work out some simple probabilities using the idea of equally likely outcomes.

 Did you know that...?

The study of probability began properly in the 17th century when the French mathematicians **Pierre de Fermat** and **Blaise Pascal** wrote letters to each other about it. But people have been aware of ideas of probability for thousands of years. Gambling and games of chance were popular activities in many ancient civilisations.

The probability of rolling three sixes is $\frac{1}{216}$.

In a probability situation, the possible things that can happen are called **outcomes**.

When the probability of each outcome is equal, they are called **equally likely outcomes**.

Probabilities can be calculated as fractions using equally likely outcomes.

Example

A fair spinner has eight equal sections numbered from 1 to 8.
If I spin the arrow, what is the probability of it landing on 7?

There are eight equally likely outcomes, each with a probability of $\frac{1}{8}$.

So the probability of getting a 7 is $\frac{1}{8}$.

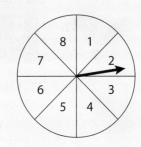

Exercise 2

1. A fair 12-sided dice is thrown.
   a List all the equally likely outcomes.
   b How many are there?
   c What is the probability of getting a score of 1 with this dice?

2. This is a fair spinner.
   a How many equally likely outcomes are there?
   b What is the probability of getting red on this spinner?
   c What is the probability of getting blue on this spinner?
   d What can you say about the probabilities for all the colours on this spinner?

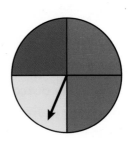

3 a Design your own spinner which uses six colours, each of which is equally likely.
   b Write a sentence to describe the probability of getting one of the colours on your spinner.

4 This spinner is spun and a coin is flipped.

   Are you more likely to get a head on the coin or yellow on the spinner?

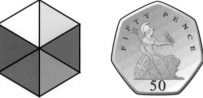

5 Look at these two fair spinners.
   a On each spinner, what is the probability of getting green?
   b Which spinner has the best chance of getting green? Explain your answer.

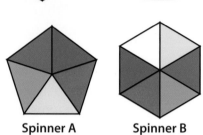

Spinner A   Spinner B

6 Here are a fair spinner and a fair dice.

   Write down an outcome on the spinner and a score on the dice that have the same probability of occurring.

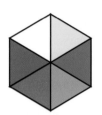 

7 Harry chose a tin of soup at random.

What is the probability that he chose a tin of pea soup?

Extension problem

8 There are six balls in a bag.
   The probability of taking a red ball out of the bag is $\frac{1}{2}$.

   A red ball is taken out of the bag, and put to one side.
   What is the probability of taking another red ball out of the bag?

Points to remember

⊙ You can use fractions to describe probabilities.
  A chance of 1 in 3 is a probability of $\frac{1}{3}$.

⊙ **Equally likely outcomes** have the same chance of happening.
  For **6** equally likely outcomes, each outcome has a probability of $\frac{1}{6}$.

3 Probability experiments

This lesson will help you to do some simple probability experiments.

Sometimes we do experiments to work out probabilities.

This might be because we cannot work out the probability using equally likely outcomes.

Example

Faysal flips a coin 50 times and records the results in a table.

Outcome	Tally	Frequency
Head	卌 卌 卌 卌 卌 卌 I	31
Tail	卌 卌 卌 IIII	19

In this experiment, Faysal has got more heads than tails.

What is the experimental probability of getting a head?

Faysal gets 31 heads out of 50 flips so the probability of getting a head is $\frac{31}{50}$.

What is the experimental probability of getting a tail?

Faysal gets 19 heads out of 50 flips so the probability of getting a tail is $\frac{19}{50}$.

Exercise 3A

Your group will need coloured cubes or counters, a bag or small box and a copy of **S3.2 Resource sheet 3.1**.

Experiment 1

- Put four cubes, each of a different colour, in your box or bag.
- Take turns to pick a cube without looking.
  Record its colour in the table on
  Resource sheet 3.1.
  Replace the cube in the bag or box.
- Repeat the experiment until you have picked a cube 50 times in total.

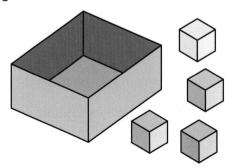

Count up how many of each colour cube you picked.
Complete the frequency column in the table.

Now write down the experimental probability of getting each of the four colours.

Experiment 2

- Put four cubes, three of one colour and one of another, in your box or bag.

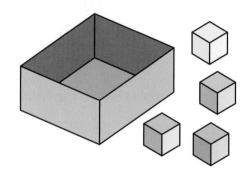

- Take turns to pick a cube without looking. Record its colour in the table on **Resource sheet 3.1**. Replace the cube in the bag or box.

- Repeat the experiment until you have picked a cube 50 times in total.

Count up how many of each colour cube you picked.
Complete the frequency column in the table.

Now write down the experimental probability of getting each of the two colours.

Exercise 3B

1. Work in a group of five or six.
   Each group will need three dice. Each person will need ten counters.

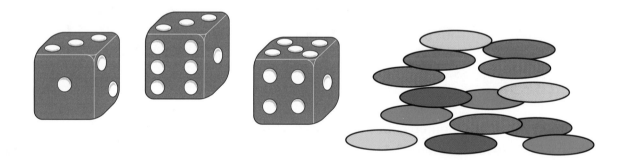

Rules

- Give each person a number from 1 to 6, so that each person has a different number.
  If there are only five people in your group, miss out the number 6.
  If there are only four people, miss out the numbers 5 and 6.

- Take turns to roll the three dice.

- Each time a player's number comes up in a throw, they must put a counter in the middle of the table.

  For example, for a score 2, 4, 4, the player with the number 2 puts in one counter and the player with the number 4 puts two counters.

- The winner is the first player to run out of counters.

Extension problems

2 The tickets in a raffle are green or blue.

These tickets are sold:

green ticket numbers **1 to 20**

blue ticket numbers **1 to 30**

a Calculate the probability that the winning ticket has the number **28** on it.

b Calculate the probability that the winning ticket has the number **14** on it.

c Calculate the probability that the ticket for the first prize is **blue**.

3 Wendy bought 6 packets of sweet pea seeds.
There were 10 seeds in each packet.

Wendy grew the seeds in identical conditions.
40 of the seeds germinated.

Estimate the probability of a sweet pea seed
will germinate.

4 Here is some information about all the pupils in a class.

	Girls	Boys
Right-handed	15	12
Left-handed	1	2

A teacher is going to choose a pupil from the class at random.

a What is the probability that the pupil chosen will be a girl?

b What is the probability that the pupil chosen will be right-handed?

Points to remember

⊙ You can estimate probability from an experiment.

⊙ The estimate may not be the same as the probability you
calculate using equally likely outcomes.

How well are you doing?

Probability

1 *2002 level 4*

I throw a fair coin.
For each statement below, write **True** or **False.**

a On each throw, the probability of getting a head is $\frac{1}{2}$. Explain your answer.

b On four throws, it is certain that I will get two heads and two tails. Explain your answer.

2 *2003 level 4*

a Gill puts 4 counters in a bag.
3 counters are red. 1 counter is white.

Gill is going to take a counter out of the bag without looking.

What is the probability that the counter will be white?

b Sam puts 20 counters in a different bag.
She is going to take a counter out of the bag without looking.

The probability that the counter will be red is $\frac{1}{2}$.
How many red counters are in her bag?

3 *1998 KS2 level 5*

A fair dice is rolled. It has the numbers 2, 2, 2, 2, 5 and 5 on it.
Which arrow which shows the probability of getting a 2?

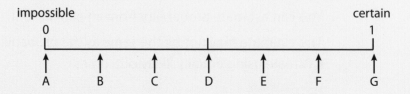

(4) *Level 5*

Ashton has a bag of jelly beans.

Contents
2 orange jelly beans
4 green jelly beans
6 pink jelly beans
5 purple jelly beans
3 yellow jelly beans

He is going to take a sweet from the bag at random.

a What is the probability that Ashton will get a yellow jelly bean?

b What is the missing colour in the sentence below?

The probability that Ashton will get a .... jelly bean is $\frac{1}{4}$.

(5) *2004 level 5*

I buy a box of different size plasters.
Assume each plaster is equally likely to be the top plaster inside the box.

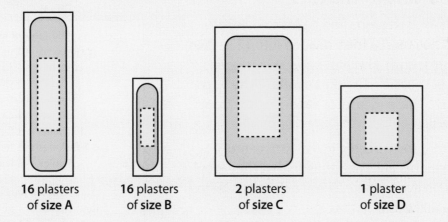

16 plasters
of **size A**   16 plasters
of **size B**   2 plasters
of **size C**   1 plaster
of **size D**

Altogether there are 35 plasters.

I take the top plaster from inside the box.

a What is the probability that the plaster is of size D?

b What is the probability that the plaster is of size A?

Decimals and measures

This unit will help you to:

- estimate measurements;
- change one metric unit to another (e.g. grams to kilograms);
- read measuring scales;
- multiply and divide whole numbers and decimals;
- use the memory of a calculator;
- check answers in different ways;
- solve word problems involving measures, including time.

1 Estimating and converting measurements

This lesson will help you to estimate measurements and to change one unit to another.

 Did you know that...?

The Romans used seeds and beans to measure weights. They used a **foot**, divided into 12 **inches**, to measure length. Five feet equalled one **pace**. 1000 paces measured a Roman **mile** (close to our mile today). These measures varied widely from place to place.

In England, a royal decree in the 13th century defined weights and measures so that they would be the same everywhere. These definitions lasted for nearly 600 years.

In the late 18th century in France, a system based on a **metre** and a **gram** developed. This system spread. Seventeen countries signed up to using it in 1875. More followed as the years went by.

Today, the United States, Liberia and Myanmar are the only countries in the world that have not switched officially to the metric system.

The UK is not entirely metric. Some old measures, called **imperial measures**, are still allowed, such as miles and pints.

Old table of length

3 barleycorns = 1 inch
12 inches = 1 foot
3 feet = 1 yard
$5\frac{1}{2}$ yards = 1 rod, pole, or perch
4 rods = 1 chain
10 chains = 1 furlong
8 furlongs = 1 mile
3 miles = 1 league

Liquid measure

5 fluid ounces = 1 gill
4 gills = 1 pint
2 pints = 1 quart
4 quarts = 1 gallon
6 gallons = 1 bulk barrel

Weight

16 drachms = 1 ounce
16 ounces = 1 pound
14 pounds = 1 stone
2 stones = 1 quarter
4 quarters = 1 hundredweight
20 hundredweights = 1 ton

It is helpful to know the measurements of common objects. You can use these to help you estimate other measurements. Here are some examples.

Your ruler is probably 30 cm long.

An apple weighs about 200 g.

A coffee mug holds about 300 ml.

Exercise 1A

① Which of these statements could be correct? Write **Yes** or **No**.

a   Julie walks 300 metres to school.

b   This biro is 100 millimetres long.

c   A recipe for a cake says use 150 grams of butter.

d   The height of the classroom is 1000 millimetres.

e   Peter cycles 50 kilometres to school.

f   My new baby brother weighs 45 grams.

g   Khalid is 3 metres tall.

h   My pencil case is 20 centimetres long.

i   Mum put 50 millilitres of petrol in her car.

j   The can of orange drink holds 350 millilitres.

② Write **A**, **B**, **C** or **D** for each of these.

a   The mass of an average-sized banana is:

    A   2 g   B   20 g   C   200 g   D   2000 g

b   The petrol tank of a new car holds:

    A   50 ml   B   500 ml   C   50 l   D   500 l

c   A dose of cough medicine is:

    A   1 ml   B   15 ml   C   150 ml   D   500 ml

d   A hen's egg weighs:

    A   50 g   B   100 g   C   200 g   D   250 g

e   The width of the classroom is:

    A   8 mm   B   8 cm   C   8 metres   D   8 km

f The capacity of a saucepan is:

A 10 ml B 20 ml

C 200 ml D 2 l

g The diameter of a saucepan is:

A 20 mm B 50 mm

C 20 cm D 50 cm

h A tin of beans holds:

A 400 grams B 400 ounces C 400 pounds D 400 kilograms

i In an hour I can walk:

A 40 metres B 4 miles C 4000 inches D 400 metres

j A gallon of water is about:

A 2 litres B 5 litres C 20 litres D 50 litres

Exercise 1B

Use this diagram to help you to convert units of length.

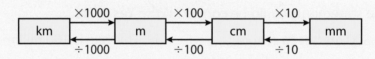

These diagrams will help you to convert units of mass or capacity.

① Write each set in order, starting with the smallest.

a 2 kg 0.2 kg 20 g b $\frac{1}{20}$ m 25 mm 20 cm

c $\frac{1}{4}$ litre 0.2 litre 400 ml d 1.1 m 109 cm 999 mm

e $\frac{3}{4}$ kg 0.7 kg 725 g f 0.5 m 50 m 0.005 km

② Here is a list of the dry ingredients for a fruit cake.

Write the list of ingredients for 10 fruit cakes.
Write each amount in kilograms.

Fruit cake ...
230 g flour
120 g sugar
150 g butter
125 g currants
70 g chopped peel
5 g spice

Nasreen, Gopal and Laura measured the same objects. The table on the right shows Nasreen's measurements.

a Gopal wrote his measurements in millimetres. What did he write?

b Laura wrote her measurements in metres. What did she write?

Object	Measurement (cm)
width of door	78
length of classroom	830
height of laptop	25
width of ruler	3.7
length of pen	20
width of eraser	2.8

Points to remember

- Multiply by 1000 to change:
  - kilograms to grams;
  - kilometres to metres;
  - metres to millimetres;
  - litres to millilitres;

- Divide by 1000 to change:
  - grams to kilograms;
  - metres to kilometres;
  - millimetres to metres;
  - millilitres to litres.

2 Reading scales

This lesson will help you to read measuring scales.

Study a scale carefully to work out the value of each interval.

Example

What is the total weight of the apples on these scales?

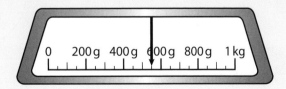

The arrow is pointing between 400 g and 600 g.
There is 200 g between 400 g and 600 g.
There are four intervals between 400 g and 600 g.
Each interval is 200 g ÷ 4 = 50 g.
Counting from 400 g in steps of 50 g takes you to 550 g.

1 Give each answer in litres and in millilitres.

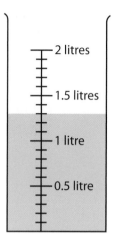

   a What does each interval represent on this measuring jar?

   b How much water is in the jar?

   c How much more water is needed to make 2 litres?

   d How much water would need to be poured out of the jar to leave 300 ml?

   e 650 millilitres of water is poured out of the jar. How much water is left in the jar?

2 How many grams of sugar are on the scales?

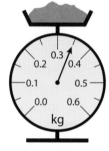

3 800 grams of flour are taken off the scales. How much flour is left?

4 Roughly what measurement is shown on the bathroom scales?

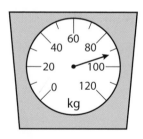

5 The diagram shows part of a ruler.
What is the distance between the two arrows in millimetres?

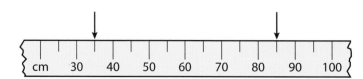

6 200 ml more water is poured into the cylinder.
How much water is in the cylinder now?

7 Here are a pencil sharpener, a key and a box of paper clips.

Actual size

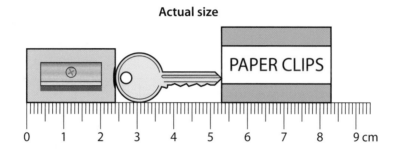

a What is the total length in millimetres of all three things together?

b What is the length in millimetres of the key?

c What is the length in millimetres of the box of paper clips?

8 Write the number shown by the red arrow on each of these lines.

a

b

c

d

e

f

Discuss questions 9 and 10 with a partner before you write your answers.

9 What unit would you choose to measure each of these?

a the distance from Leeds to Liverpool
b the amount of water in a home hot water tank
c the perimeter of the classroom
d the mass of a carrot
e the distance from Earth to the Moon
f the thickness of glass in a window pane
g the contents of a tin of soup
h the width of a book
i the mass of a paper clip
j the mass of a van
k the capacity of a teaspoon
l the length of a swimming pool

Extension problem

10 What units of measurement might you see in these places?

a a TV weather forecast
b a supermarket
c a garage
d a railway station
e a chemist's shop
e a car park

Points to remember

⊙ To work out the quantity represented by an interval on a scale:
– find two numbered divisions;
– work out their difference;
– divide the difference by the number of intervals between the divisions.

3 Solving word problems

This lesson will help you to solve word problems involving measures and to check your answers.

When you solve word problems, make sure that all measurements are in the same unit before your write down your calculation. Remember to check your answer.

Example

Dad buys a 1.2 kg bag of carrots. He uses 465 g to make some soup.
How many grams of carrots are left?

1.2 kg = 1200 g. Change both to grams.
Start with: 1200 g Use: 465 g
Now work out $1200 - 465 = 735$.
Check the answer by adding $735 + 465 = 1200$
Answer: 735 grams

1 **Length**

Give your answer to each question in (i) centimetres, and (ii) metres.

a   A model of a truck is 60 cm long. Its trailer is 45 cm long.
     What is the total length of the truck and the trailer?

b   A toy train has an engine and six identical carriages.
     The engine is 20 cm long and the carriages are 15 cm long.
     What is the total length of the train?

c   A truck is 3 m 70 cm tall. It goes under an arch of height 4.2 m.
     What is the size of the gap between the top of the truck and the arch?

2 **Mass**

Give your answer to each question in kilograms.

a   There is 700 g of rice in a jar. I put in 2.5 kg more rice.
     How much rice is in the jar now?

b   I had 2.25 kg of sugar. I used 750 g to make jam,
     and 350 g to make a cake.
     How much sugar do I have left?

c   Ajit and Mira check in at the airport.
     Mira's suitcase weighs 24.25 kg.
     Ajit puts his suitcase besides Mira's on the scales.
     The total weight of both suitcases is 49.2 kg.

     What is the weight of Ajit's suitcase?

3 **Capacity**

a   A cup holds 225 ml of soup. How many cups of soup can you get from 1.5 litres?

b   The petrol tank in Peter's car has a capacity of 45 litres.
     His father's car holds $2\frac{1}{2}$ times as much.
     What is the capacity of his father's petrol tank?

c   A dose of medicine is two 5 ml teaspoons
     three times a day. How much medicine must
     you take each day?

     The medicine bottle holds 150 ml.
     How many days will the medicine last?

(4) **Area and perimeter**

a The area of a postage stamp is 6.25 cm².
A sheet of postage stamps measures 25 cm by 15 cm.
How many postage stamps are on the sheet?

b A gardener wants to put an edging around a 10 metre square lawn.
The edging costs £3.50 per metre.
How much must the gardener pay for the edging?

c A box of fertiliser covers 15 square metres of grass.
How many boxes must a gardener buy to fertilise a lawn of 100 square metres?

Exercise 3B

Solve these problems. You may **use a calculator** but write down the calculation that you will do to solve each problem.

(1) Sue bought a 2.75 m plank of wood.
She sawed off 80 cm to make a shelf.
What is the length of the remaining plank of wood?

(2) A bottle of salad dressing holds 0.3 litre.
A tablespoon holds 15 ml.

How many tablespoons of dressing are in the bottle?

(3) There is 365 ml of milk in a jug.
Another 450 ml of milk is added.
How much milk is in the jug now?

(4) Each side of a regular octagon is 14 cm long.
What is the length of its perimeter in metres?

(5) A theatre has 400 litres of coffee for refreshments for the audience in the interval.
One mug of coffee is 250 ml.
How many of the audience can have a mug of coffee?

(6) 2.76 kg of flour are on the scales.
How many grams of flour must be added to make
3 kg altogether?

(7) Greg uses 2 apples to make half a litre of apple sauce.
How much sauce can he make from 14 apples?

(8) A rectangular field is 0.3 km long and 250 m wide.
What is the length of its perimeter?

(9) A pin is made from 14 mm of wire.
What is the greatest number of pins that can be made from 1 m of wire?

(10) A garage orders 50 000 litres of petrol. It sells an average of 1250 litres per day.
How long does its supply of petrol last?

Extension problem

(11) Mary is tiling 2.5 square metres of her bathroom wall.
How many 10 cm by 10 cm tiles does she need?

⊙ Points to remember

- ⊙ To solve word problems:
  - look out for key words that help to decide what operation(s) to do;
  - change all measurements to the same unit;
  - check your answer;
  - make sure the answer is sensible in the context;
  - include any units in the answer.

4 Problems involving time

This lesson will help you to solve problems involving time.

Use this chart to convert between seconds, minutes, hours, days and weeks.

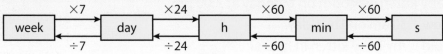

The 24-hour clock time 13:26 means 1:26 pm.
The 24-hour clock time 06:45 means 6:45 am.
Time lines are useful for working out time intervals.

Example

Mr Jones left Bobby at his nursery at 9:40 am.
He collected Bobby at 2:35 pm.
How long was Bobby at the nursery?

Method 1

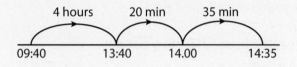

Count up from 09:40 to 14:35.
4 hours + 20 minutes + 35 minutes
Answer: 4 hours 55 minutes

Method 2

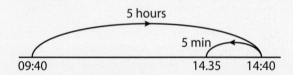

Count in hours from 09:40 to 14:40, until you
have gone too far, then adjust.
5 hours − 5 minutes
Answer: 4 hours 55 minutes

Exercise 4

1 a How many days are there in seven weeks and one day?

   b How many months are there in $7\frac{1}{2}$ years?

   c A TV programme lasts 45 minutes.
      How many seconds is this?

   d How many hours are there in April?

   e My birthday is 22 days after my friend's birthday.
      My friend's birthday is on 20 April.
      This year it was on a Friday.
      On what day was my birthday?

> **Old English rhyme**
>
> *Thirty days has September,*
> *April, June and November.*
> *All the rest have thirty-one*
> *Excepting February alone,*
> *Which has but twenty-eight days clear,*
> *And twenty-nine each leap year.*

2 A film starts at 19:45.
   It lasts 2 hours and 35 minutes.
   At what time will the film finish?

3 My baby kitten was born on Monday at 3:00 pm.
   It is now 7:30 am on Thursday.
   How old is my baby kitten in hours?

4 Here are the start and finish times of some people doing a sponsored walk. How much longer did Callum take than Lucy?

	Start time	Finish time
Callum	9:30	10:55
Sean	9:35	11:05
Amanda	9:40	11:08
Lucy	9:45	11:05

5 Ali is travelling in the Middle East. He looks at part of a train timetable.

Dharan	—	0935	—	—	1335	—	—
Al Mubarraz	0915	—	1115	1315	—	1345	1515
Al Hufuf	0957	—	1157	1357	—	1429	1557
Harad	1034	1051	1234	1434	1450	1515	1635
Riyadh	—	1310	—	—	1705	—	—

a How long does the first train from Dharan take to travel to Riyadh?

b Ali is at Al Mubarraz station at half past one in the afternoon.
He catches the next train to Harad.
At what time will he arrive in Harad?

Ali looks at the timetable showing the bus times from Madinat to Doha.

c How long does the 1603 bus take from Umm Salal to Doha?

d Ali is in Madinat.
He needs to be in Umm Salal before noon. What is the latest bus he should catch?

e How long does the 0943 bus take from Madinat to Umm Salal?

Madinat	0744	0906	0943	1406
Al Kaban	0835	0938	1015	
Al Khawr	0927	1027	1127	1527
Umm Salal	1003	1103	1203	1603
Ar Rayyan	1109			1709
Doha	1147	1246	1342	1750

6   Here are some car park charges.

a   Tom parks at 8:30 am. He leaves at noon.
How much does he pay?

b   Rachel parks at 11:50. She leaves at 00:20.
How much does she pay?

c   How much does it cost to park for 3 hours
a day from Monday to Friday?

d   Molly left the car park at 2:15 pm.
She paid £2.30. If she had left 5 minutes earlier
she would have paid 80p.
At what time did she park her car?

Car park charges	
Time	Charge
up to 1 hour	35p
1 to 2 hours	80p
2 to 4 hours	£2.30
4 to 24 hours	£5.50
over 24 hours	£10

Extension problem

7   The table shows how much
time it takes to fly between
some cities.

For example, it takes
1 hour 3 minutes to fly from
Paris to London.

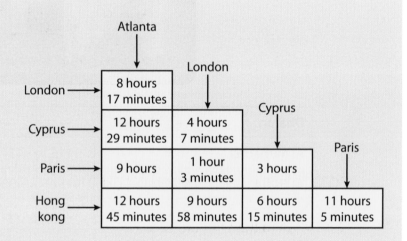

	Atlanta	London	Cyprus	Paris
London	8 hours 17 minutes			
Cyprus	12 hours 29 minutes	4 hours 7 minutes		
Paris	9 hours	1 hour 3 minutes	3 hours	
Hong kong	12 hours 45 minutes	9 hours 58 minutes	6 hours 15 minutes	11 hours 5 minutes

a   A flight leaves Paris at
11:50 London time.
At what time does it arrive
in London?

b   Time in Atlanta is 5 hours behind London.
What is the time in Atlanta when it is 02:15 in London ?

c   A flight from Cyprus to Hong Kong arrives in Hong Kong at 1545.
What was the time in Hong Kong when the flight left Cyprus?

d   Nora's flight leaves London at 07:00.
What time will it be in London when Nora is due to land in Atlanta?

e   James flies from Atlanta to London, where he stays overnight.
In the morning, he flies on from London to Hong Kong.
What is his total flight time?

Points to remember

⊙ Time lines are useful for working out time intervals.
⊙ The 24-hour clock time 13:26 means 1:26 pm, and 06:45 means 6:45 am.

5 Multiplication and division calculations

This lesson will help you to multiply and divide whole numbers and decimals and check your answers.

Use an efficient method to multiply or divide numbers. Use rounding to estimate the answer.

Example 1   Estimate the answer to 586×41.

An approximate answer is $600 \times 40 = 2400$.

Example 2   Calculate 236×47.

Estimate the answer as $200 \times 50 = 10\,000$.
$11\,092$ is close to $10\,000$ so is likely to be correct.

$$
\begin{array}{r}
236 \\
\times\ 47 \\
\hline
9440 \quad (236 \times 40) \\
+\ 1652 \quad (236 \times 7) \\
\hline
11092
\end{array}
$$

Answer: $236 \times 47 = 11\,092$

Example 3   Calculate $864 \div 32$.

Estimate the answer as $900 \div 30 = 30$.
27 is close to the estimate so is likely to be right.

$$
\begin{array}{r}
27 \\
32\overline{)864} \\
-640 \quad 32 \times 20 \\
\hline
224 \\
-224 \quad 32 \times 7 \\
\hline
0
\end{array}
$$

Answer: $864 \div 32 = 27$

Exercise 5A

1. Estimate the answers.
   a 162×31 b $237 \div 39$ c 58.1×9.9 d $44.8 \div 4.75$

2. Work these out **without using a calculator.**
   a 362×60 b 437×54 c 213×39 d 84×208

3. Work these out **without using a calculator.**
   a $896 \div 32$ b $616 \div 28$ c $468 \div 39$ d $768 \div 16$

Use an efficient method to multiply or divide decimals by a one-digit number.
Estimate the answer first.

Example 1 9.42×6

The answer lies between $9 \times 6 = 54$ and $10 \times 6 = 60$.

$9.42 \times 6 = 942 \times 6 \div 100$. Work out 942×6, then divide
the answer of 5652 by 100 to get 56.52.

56.52 lies between 54 and 60 so is likely to be correct.

$$\begin{array}{r} 942 \\ \times\ 6 \\ \hline 5652 \\ {\scriptstyle 2\ 1} \end{array}$$

Answer: $9.42 \times 6 = 56.52$

Example 2 $39.2 \div 7$

The answer lies between $35 \div 7 = 5$ and $42 \div 7 = 6$.
The calculation is equivalent to $392 \div 7$ divided by 10. The answer
to $392 \div 7$ is 56, so the answer to $39.2 \div 7$ is 5.6.
5.6 lies between 6 and 7 so is likely to be correct.

$$\begin{array}{r} 56 \\ 7\overline{)392} \\ -350 \\ \hline 42 \\ -42 \\ \hline 0 \end{array}$$

Answer: $39.2 \div 7 = 5.6$

---

1   Play **Target** with a partner.

You need one calculator between you.

Take turns to go first.

The aim is to get a number in the display as
close as possible to 100.

Rules

◉ Take turns.

◉ Clear the display, enter a starting number
between 0 and 20, and pass the calculator
to the other player.

◉ The other player multiplies the number in
the display by their chosen number, then
presses =.

◉ An answer from 95 to 105, including
decimals, scores 1 point.

◉ The winner is the first to get 4 points.

Example

Ann enters 14.5.
Jo multiplies by 7 to get 101.5.
Jo scores 1 point.

$14.5 \times 7 = 101.5$

Jo clears the display and enters 16.
Ann multiplies by 6.8 to get 108.8.

$16 \times 6.8 = 108.8$

Ann gets no score.

2 Do these calculations **without using a calculator**. Estimate first.

  a 49.8 × 7   b 3.67 × 5   c 9.52 ÷ 8   d 78.4 ÷ 7

 Points to remember

 ⊙ Look first to see if you can do a calculation in your head.
 ⊙ Use an efficient written method if no calculator is available.
 ⊙ Always estimate the answer to multiplication and division calculations.
 ⊙ Check the answer by using the inverse operation.

6 Solving problems with a calculator

This lesson will help you to use a calculator to solve problems.

The memory of a calculator can be useful. On some calculators the three main keys are:

[M+] This key adds the number in the display to the memory.

[M−] This key subtracts the number in the display from the memory.
    On some calculators this is [SHIFT] [M+].

[MR] or [RCL] This key puts the number in the memory in the display.

Example

Find the total cost of 5 pairs of socks at £2.79 each and 3 T-shirts at £8.45 each.
Here is one way to use your calculator if it has an [M+] and an [MR] or [RCL] key.

Step 1: Switch on, or press [ON/c]. This clears the display and the memory.

Step 2: Enter [5][×][2][·][7][9][=]
    You will see 13.95 in the display.

Step 3: Press [M+] to add 13.95 to the memory.

Step 4: Clear the display by pressing the clear key.
    A small M may indicate a number in the memory.

Step 5: Enter [3][×][8][·][4][5][=]
    You will see 25.35 in the display.

Step 6: Press [M+] to add 25.35 to the memory.

Step 7: Press the memory recall button.
    The total of 39.3 will appear in the display. This means **£39.30.**

1 What is the final number in the display after these key sequences? Write down your prediction.

a ON/C 6 M+ 6 M+ 6 M+ MR

b ON/C 9 × 5 M+ 2 0 M− MR

c ON/C 6 × 2 M+ 5 × 4 M+ MR

d ON/C 5 0 M+ 3 × 5 M− MR

e ON/C 1 5 M+ M+ MR M+ MR

If you calculator has M+ , M− and MR keys, check with your calculator.

2 Use a calculator to solve these problems. Write down the calculation that you do.

a The sides of a rectangle are 2.8 and 5.6 cm. Calculate its perimeter.

b Clare bought four tins of beans at 39p each,
seven oranges at 28p each
and five bananas at 26p each.
How much did she pay altogether?

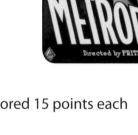

c Cinema tickets cost £4.85 for adults and £2.65 for
children under 14.
What is the total cost of tickets for 2 adults and
3 children?

d Harry bought four DVDs at £5.72 each.
How much change did he get from £30?

e A class of 29 pupils played a game.
Seven pupils scored 12 points each, thirteen pupils scored 15 points each
and nine pupils scored 17 points each.
What was the total score for the class?

3 In these calculations, each ✳ stands for a missing digit. Find the missing digits.

a ✳7 × 9 = 333   b ✳92 ÷ 14 = 28

c 323 × ✳7 = 15 18✳   d ✳✳✳ × ✳ = 215

4 Make 9.

Use only these keys on your calculator, once each, in any order. When you press the equals key, the number 9 should appear in the display.

$$\boxed{1}\boxed{2}\boxed{3}\boxed{4}\boxed{5}\boxed{6}\boxed{7}\boxed{8}\boxed{9}\boxed{+}\boxed{-}\boxed{=}$$

Record how you did it.

Extension problem

5 Put plus or minus signs in suitable places in this expression to make it correct.

$$1\ 2\ 3\ 4\ 5\ 6\ 7\ 8\ 9 = 100$$

You can push the digits together to make a two- or three-digit number but you must not change their order. Here is one way to do it.

$$12 + 3 - 4 + 5 + 67 + 8 + 9 = 100$$

Record your solution then find other ways to do it.

◉ Points to remember

- The memory of a calculator can be useful when solving problems. For example, it can be used to keep a total.

How well are you doing?

Can you:

- change one metric unit to another (e.g. grams to kilograms)?
- estimate measurements, and compare or calculate with them by changing them to the same units??
- read measuring scales?
- solve word problems involving measures, including time?
- multiply and divide whole numbers and decimals?

Measurements and decimals (no calculator)

1 Write the answers.

    a How many grams are there in 12 kilograms?

    b How many metres are there in 1.5 kilometres?

    c How many millilitres are there in two and a half litres?

    d How many square millimetres are there in one square centimetre?

2 *2002 KS2 level 4*

This table shows the weights of some fruits and vegetables.

Copy and complete the table.

	grams	kilograms
potatoes	3500	
apples		1.2
grapes	250	
ginger		0.03
carrots	600	

3 Write A, B, C or D for each of these.

    a The kettle in my kitchen holds:

       A 2 litres   B 20 litres   C 200 litres   D 2000 litres

    b The height of the door to my room is:

       A 2 millilitres   B 2 centimetres   C 2 metres   D 2 kilometres

    c The apple I will eat for lunch weighs:

       A 1 gram   B 10 grams   C 100 grams   D 1000 grams

(4) Calculate these.

    a 924 ÷ 22
                             b 509 × 24

(5) **a** An aeroplane takes off on Monday at 23:56.
      It lands on Tuesday at 06:10.
      How long was the flight?

    b Kelly buys a pack of 24 cans of cola for £6.00.
      What is the cost of each can?

Measurements and decimals (calculator allowed)

(6) *1999 KS2 level 5*

Here is a drawing of a model car.

    a What is the length of the model?
      Give your answer in centimetres, correct to one decimal place.

    b The height of the model is 2.8 centimetres.
      The height of the real car is 50 times the height of the model.
      What is the height of the real car? Give your answer in metres.

(7) **a** A bottle holds 2 litres of lemonade.
      Maria fills 5 glasses with lemonade.
      She puts 230 millilitres in each glass.
      How much lemonade is left in the bottle?

    b A packet contains 1.2 kilograms of pet food.
      Tracey feeds her pet mice 50 grams of pet food each day.
      How many days does the packet of food last?

(8) In these calculations, each ◆ stands for a missing digit.
Find the missing digits.

    a ◆0 × ◆0 = 3000
                            b ◆34 × ◆ = ◆◆0

Equations and formulae

> **This unit will help you to:**
>
> ⊙ simplify algebraic expressions;
>
> ⊙ substitute numbers into expressions and formulae;
>
> ⊙ solve simple equations.

1 Terms and expressions

This lesson will help you to understand words used in algebra.

These are all **terms**: 5, 63, $2a$, $6x$, $5y$, $4ab$, $3lw$

Like terms have the same combination of letters.

An **algebraic expression** is a collection of terms. Example: $5 + 3x + 2y$

Example 1

Write down the four terms of the expression $3x + y - 2z + 6$.

The four terms are $3x$ and y and $-2z$ and 6.

Example 2

A box contains p plain chocolates and q milk chocolates.

Write an expression for the total number of chocolates in the box.

The total number of chocolates in the box is $p + q$.

Exercise 1

① Copy these expressions. Underline each term.

   a $5 + 3m$ b $6p + 8q + 5r$

   c $3x + 4y - 7z$ d $24 - 3w + 4x - 3y$

   e $2xy + 5xz + 7yz$ f $7a + 3b + 5c - 4bc + 6ac + 2abc$

② Work out the value of each of expression when $x = 5$ and $y = 4$.

   a $x + y$ b $y + x$ c $x + y - 3$

   d $x - y$ e $y - x$ f $2x + y$

   g $2x + 2y + 7$ h $2x - 3y + 2$ i $2xy + 1$

③ A class has x boys and y girls.
Write an expression for the total number of pupils in the class.

④ Andy swims a metres and Bill swims b metres. Bill swims further than Andy.
Write an expression for the number of metres Bill swims further than Andy.

⑤ Jane buys b apples. She then eats c of them.
Write an expression for the number of apples Jane has left.

⑥ Marbles are sold in bags and boxes.
There are p marbles in each bag
and q marbles in each box.

Simon buys four bags and three boxes.

   a Write an expression for the total number
of marbles Simon buys.

   b Simon then gives 10 marbles to James.
Write an expression for the total number
of marbles Simon has left.

⑦ Simplify these expressions by collecting like terms.

   a $3x + 4x$ b $y + 7y + 6y$

   c $2p + 3p + p$ d $6w + 3w - 5w$

   e $2z + z + 5z + 8z$ f $6x - x$

   g $14y + 3y + 5y + 2y - 4y$ h $5x + 9x + x + 4x - 2x$

Extension problem

⑧ Simplify these expressions by collecting like terms.

   a $9p + 2q + 6p + 5q$ b $6x + 2y + 5x + 7y + x$

   c $2ab + 5ab + 7ab + 6ab$ d $8x + 2y + 3z + 6x + 4y - 3z$

   e $9 + 3z + z + 7z + 8$ f $5ax + 6bx + 4ax + 9bx$

Points to remember

- $3n + 5$ is an **expression**. An algebraic expression must contain at least one letter.
- Each part of an expression is called a **term** of the expression. For example, for the expression $3n + 5$ the terms are $3n$ and 5.
- **Like terms** have the same combination of letters. For example, $2x$ and $5x$ and x are all like terms.

2 Multiplying terms in brackets

This lesson will help you to simplify algebraic expressions by multiplying out brackets.

$5(n + 3)$ means five times n and five times 3.

$\times$	$n + 3$
5	$5n + 15$

Example

Multiply out $5(2x + 3)$.

$$5(2x + 3) = 5 \times 2x + 5 \times 3$$
$$= 10x + 15$$

Exercise 2

1. Multiply out these brackets.
   - a $3(n + 7)$
   - b $6(n + 9)$
   - c $4(n - 8)$
   - d $2(x + 10)$
   - e $5(x - 9)$
   - f $9(y + 4)$
   - g $10(x - 7)$
   - h $12(y + 3)$

2. Multiply out these brackets.
   - a $2(3n + 2)$
   - b $5(4n - 3)$
   - c $6(5x + 7)$
   - d $7(8y + 9)$
   - e $3(7x + 3)$
   - f $8(4y - 6)$
   - g $10(9p + 11)$
   - h $9(7q - 10)$

3. Simplify these expressions by collecting like terms.
   - a $2a + 4a$
   - b $5b + 2b + 1$
   - c $6m - 4m$
   - d $2p + 3p + 5 - 1$
   - e $3 + 7b + 2 + 2b$
   - f $2c + 1 + 4c - 2$
   - g $3y - 2y + 3 - y + 5$
   - h $4 - 2m + 4m + 1$
   - i $3y - 4y$

4. Multiply out these brackets.
   - a $2(a + b)$
   - b $10(x - y)$
   - c $6(p + q + r)$
   - d $7(l + w - h)$
   - e $4(2x + 3y)$
   - f $8(5a + 4b + 3c)$

Extension problem

 5 Multiply out these brackets. Simplify your answers.

    a $2(3x + 4) + 3(5x + 2)$ **b** $4(2x - 3) + 5(7x + 6)$

    c $4(2a + 3b) + 5(3a + 2b)$ **d** $8(3x - 2y) + 3(4x - y)$

⊙ Points to remember

- ⊙ You can simplify an expression by collecting like terms.
- ⊙ $5(n + 3)$ means 5 times n and 5 times 3.

---

3 Formulae

This lesson will help you to substitute values into formulae.

A **formula** is a rule for working out a quantity. It is written using words or letters and has an equals sign.

A formula in **words** for the cost of some packets of crisps is

> **cost = number of packets × price of one packet**

If the price of a packet of crisps is x pence, a formula in **symbols** for the cost C in pence of n packets of crisps is

> $C = n \times x$

Exercise 3

 1 Packets of crisps cost 40p each. Use the formula

> **cost = number of packets of crisps × 40**

to work out the cost of 5 packets of crisps.

2 Peter works for 20 hours. He is paid an hourly rate of £6 an hour. Use the formula

pay = hourly rate × hours worked

to work out Peter's pay.

3 Here is a formula to work out the area of a rectangle in cm².

area = length in cm × width in cm

Use the formula, to work out the area of a rectangle of length 8 cm and width 3 cm.

4 A sum of money is shared equally between four friends.
The formula to work out the amount in £ that each friend gets is

amount for each friend = sum of money ÷ 4

Use the formula to work out the amount each friend gets when the sum of money is £30.

5 One orange costs p pence. James buys n oranges.
The total cost of the oranges is given by the formula

total cost = p × n pence

The price of one orange is 35p. Use the formula to work out:

a the total cost of 8 oranges   **b** the total cost of 20 oranges

6 Let the length of a rectangle be l.
Let the width of the rectangle be w.
The formula for the perimeter of the
rectangle in cm is

perimeter = $2l + 2w$ cm

Copy and complete this table.

Length l (cm)	Width w (cm)	Perimeter $2l + 2w$ (cm)
6	3	
9	7	
10	6	
9	8	

7 Let n be the number of text messages that Janine sends in a day.

Write a formula using n for each of these.

a Ryan sends twice as many text messages as Janine.

b Sarah sends ten more text messages than Janine.

c Josie sends six less text messages than Janine.

d Sam sends four times as many text messages as Janine.

e Pati send half as many text messages as Janine.

f James sends eight more text messages than Ryan.

8 Tiles are placed around squares to form a sequence of patterns.

| Pattern 1 | Pattern 2 | Pattern 3 |

 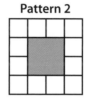 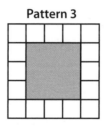

The number of white tiles in each pattern gives the sequence

    8,   12,   16,   …

a Write the next three terms in the sequence.

b What is the formula for the nth term of the sequence?

c Work out the 50th term of the sequence.

Extension problems

9 Let n be the cost of pencils and m be the cost of exercise books, both in pounds.
Write expressions for:

a the cost of 8 pencils

b the cost of 20 pencils and 50 exercise books

c how much more it will cost to buy 10 exercise books than 10 pencils

d how much change you get from £50 when you buy 25 pencils and 14 exercise books.

10 Let the length of the base of a triangle be b.
Let the height of the triangle be h.
The formula for the area of the triangle is

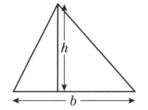

Area $= \frac{1}{2}bh$ square units

Copy and complete this table.

Base length b (cm)	Height h (cm)	Area $\frac{1}{2}bh$ (cm²)
12	5	
10	7	
15	8	
20	10	

 Points to remember

⊙ A **formula** is a way of writing a rule using letters. For example, the formula for working out the area A of a rectangle with length l and width w is $A = lw$.

4 Equations: addition and subtraction

This lesson will help you to solve equations involving addition and subtraction.

 Did you know that...?

Diophantus was a Greek mathematician who lived in the 3rd century.

He wrote some books called about solving equations so he is sometimes called 'the father of algebra'.

He was also the first Greek mathematician to recognise fractions as numbers.

This is an **equation**: $x + y = 9$.

An equation must always have an **equals sign** '='.

The expression before the equals sign is the **left-hand side** of the **equation**.

The expression after the equals sign is the **right-hand side** of the **equation**.

Everything on the left-hand side has the same value as everything on the right-hand side.

In the equation $x + y = 9$, both sides have the value 9. There is an **infinite number of solutions**.

x could be 1 and y could be 8,
x could be 2 and y could be 6, and so on.

Here is another equation: $x + 5 = 9$.

In this case there is only **one possible solution**, when $x = 4$.

Exercise 4

1. Copy and complete this table.

x	8	5		46	2.5		$\frac{3}{5}$
y	6		13			3.5	
$x + y$		12	25	130	7.4	9	$\frac{9}{5}$

2. Copy and complete this table.

x	10	14			8		$\frac{7}{5}$
y	7		8	24		5.7	
$x - y$		2	5	13	2.5	6.8	$\frac{3}{5}$

3. Find the value of x for each of these.

   a $x + 7 = 12$

   b $x + 10 = 19$

   c $x + 4 = 15$

   d $x + 21 = 40$

   e $x + 17 = 28$

   f $x + 11 = 20$

   g $x + 25 = 100$

   h $x + 1.5 = 8$

   i $x + 3.2 = 5$

4 Find the value of x for each of these.

    a $x - 2 = 5$ **b** $x - 7 = 9$ **c** $x - 12 = 25$

    d $x - 15 = 33$ **e** $x - 50 = 50$ **f** $x - 9 = 91$

    g $x - 3.5 = 2.5$ **h** $x - 0.5 = 8$ **i** $x - 2.4 = 1.6$

Extension problem

5 Here is an equation: $x + y = 8$.

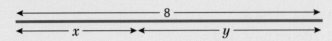

    a Write all the pairs of positive whole numbers (x, y) that satisfy this equation.

    b Write five other pairs of numbers (x, y) that satisfy the equation.
        (x and y can be fractions, decimals or negative numbers.)

● Points to remember

- These are **equations**: $x + y = 9$, $x - y = 5$. They both have an infinite number of solutions.

- These equations have only one solution.

Equation	Solution
$x + 3 = 10$	$x = 7$
$x - 4 = 5$	$x = 9$

5 Equations: multiplication and division

This lesson will help you to solve equations involving multiplication and division.

Exercise 5

1 Copy and complete this table.

x	6	7		3		4	
y	9		8		15		$\frac{2}{5}$
$x \times y$		35	72	75	60	10	2

Copy and complete this table.

x	25	49		28			
y	5		5		9	0.5	$\frac{1}{2}$
$x \div y$		7	8	4	7	14	1

3 Find the value of x for each of these.

a $5x = 30$ b $9x = 63$ c $8x = 80$ d $4x = 48$

e $7x = 35$ f $11x = 99$ g $4x = 4$ h $10x = 130$

i $20x = 100$ j $25x = 75$

4 Find the value of x for each of these.

a $x \div 4 = 7$ b $x \div 6 = 9$ c $x \div 3 = 8$ d $x \div 2 = 45$

e $x \div 5 = 12$ f $x \div 10 = 3$ g $x \div 8 = 4$ h $x \div 4 = 9$

i $x \div 5 = 8$ j $x \div 10 = 12$

Extension problem

5 Here is an equation: $xy = 18$.

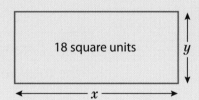

18 square units

a Write all the positive whole numbers (x, y) that satisfy this equation.

b Write five other pairs of numbers (x, y) that satisfy this equation.
   (x and y can be fractions, decimals or negative numbers.)

Points to remember

⊙ The equation $xy = 4$ has an infinite number of solutions.

⊙ These equations have only one solution.
   $6x = 18$ $x = 3$
   $x \div 5 = 3$ $x = 15$

How well are you doing?

Expressions, equations and formulae

1 *2006 level 4*

The equation shows how much you pay to hire a car.

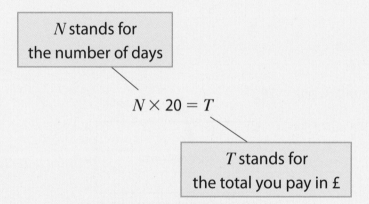

N stands for the number of days

$$N \times 20 = T$$

T stands for the total you pay in £

a Leena hires the car for 10 days. How much must she pay?

b Later, Tom pays £280 to hire the car. For how many days does he hire the car?

2 *2007 level 4*

a Look at this equation.

$$x + y = 30$$

What could the values of x and y be? Give one pair of values.

Now give a different pair of values that x and y could be.

b Here is a different equation.

$$a - b = 30$$

When $a = 40$, what is the value of b?

3 *2003 level 5*

Simplify these expressions.

a $5k + 7 + 3k$

b $k + 1 + k + 4$

4 Multiply out:

a $4(2p + 3)$

b $3(5p + 7)$

5 *2002 level 5*

When $x = 5$, work out the values of the expressions below.

a $2x + 13$

b $5x - 5$

c $3 + 6x$

6 *2006 level 5*

Solve these equations.

a $2k + 3 = 11$

b $2t + 3 = -11$

Enquiry 1

This unit will help you to:

- investigate problems by collecting and using data;
- decide what information you need to answer a question;
- plan how to collect and organise data;
- draw graphs and charts on paper or using ICT;
- interpret graphs, charts and diagrams, and say what they tell you.

1 Planning a project

This lesson will help you to decide what information you need to answer a question and where to find it.

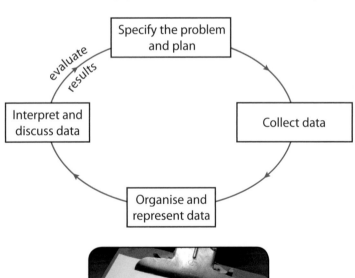

Statistical questions can have lots of different answers.

There will be different reasons that might explain each of these answers.

In order to find out the correct answer, you may need to carry out a **survey** or **experiment**.

Exercise 1

Work in a group of four or five. You will need a copy of **S3.3 Resource sheet 1.1**.

Your teacher will ask your group to think about one of these questions.

Questions

- How do most pupils travel to school?
- What do pupils spend their money on?
- Are females better at estimating lengths or angles than males?
- Do tabloid newspapers have shorter sentences than broadsheet papers?

1. In your group, think of three different possible answers to your question.
   Write them down on the resource sheet, with reasons.

2. Now think about and write down how you could find out the correct answer to the question.
   Include as much detail as you can about what you would do and how.

3. After reviewing your ideas as a class, write down any improvements you want to make to your plan for finding out the correct answer.

Points to remember

- Use the data handling cycle to plan and carry out projects.
- Plan carefully what information you need and how to collect it, e.g.
  - carry out a survey;
  - do an experiment;
  - use a source such as the Internet or books.

2 Collecting data 1

This lesson will help you to plan how to collect and organise data.

You can collect data yourself by carrying out a survey or by doing an experiment.
When you write a questionnaire, think carefully about the choices you offer.

Make sure your experiments are good tests of what you are trying to find out.

You might need to count your data and sort it into a frequency table.
This makes the data easier to analyse.
Make sure that the frequency table covers all the possible data values.

Questions

- How do most pupils travel to school?
- What do pupils spend their money on?
- Are females better at estimating lengths or angles than males?
- Do tabloid newspapers have shorter sentences than broadsheet papers?

1. Work in a group of four or five.
   You will need the copy of **S3.3 Resource sheet 1.1** that you completed in Exercise 1.

   Think again about the question you looked at in Exercise 1.
   Plan an experiment or a questionnaire to collect the data you need to answer the question.

   Now collect the data, e.g. from the rest of your class.

● Points to remember

- Plan carefully how you will collect the data.
- When you write a questionnaire, think about the choices you offer.
- Where numerical data varies widely, group the data for analysis.

3 Drawing charts and graphs using ICT

This lesson will help you to draw graphs and charts on paper or using ICT.

Bar charts, **pie charts** and **frequency diagrams** are used to represent data.
They help to reveal what the data shows.

This **bar chart** show the eye colours of 40 adults.

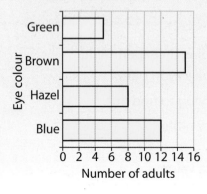

This **pie chart** shows the favourite pet of a Year 7 class.

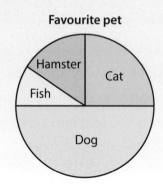

This **frequency diagram** shows the marks of 20 pupils in a test.

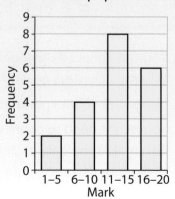

Example 1

Open the file **S3.3 Charts**.

Use Excel to draw a bar chart for the shoe size data.

Use the mouse to select the two columns and click on the chart wizard. Click through the chart wizard to step 3 where you can add a title and labels for the axes.

Use **S3.3 Resource sheet 3.1** if you need more help.

Shoe size	
Size	Frequency
one	9
two	2
three	2
four	5
five	4
six	5
seven	1
eight	0
nine	1
ten	1

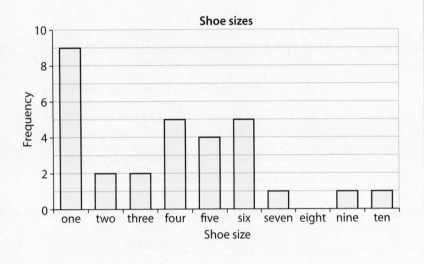

Example 2

Use Excel to draw a pie chart to show the estimating dots data.

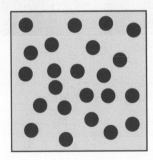

Estimating dots	
Number	Frequency
26–30	6
31–35	12
36–40	10

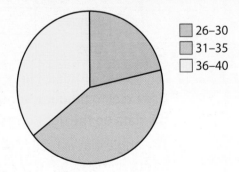

Use the mouse to select the two columns and click on the chart wizard.

Under 'Chart type' select 'Pie'.

Click through the chart wizard to step 3 where you can add a title.

To produce the frequency diagrams for the grouped data, highlight both columns in the table as for a bar chart.

Exercise 3

1　**a** Use Excel to produce bar charts and pie charts for the data on the right on travelling to school.

　b Use your graphs and charts to find out the most common method of travelling to school.

　c Do you think that most pupils live near to or far from school? Give your reasons.

Travel to school	
Method	**Frequency**
walk	8
cycle	4
car	12
train	0
bus	5
other	0

2　**a** Use Excel to produce bar charts and pie charts for the data below on spending money.

　b Use your graphs and charts to write the items money was spent on in frequency order, with the most frequent first.

　c Do you think this data is from boys, or girls, or a mixture of both? Give your reasons.

Spending money	
Item	**Frequency**
sweets	2
magazines	4
clothes	8
CDs	8
make up	3
savings	1
toys	0

3　**a** Use Excel to produce frequency diagrams for the data on the right on estimating angles.

　b The angle was actually 36°. Use your frequency diagram to write down the most popular guess for the size of the angle.

　c How good do you think people were at estimating the size of the angle? Give your reasons.

Angle estimation	
Estimate	**Frequency**
21–25	2
26–30	7
31–35	5
36–40	12
41–45	3
46–50	1

4 a Use Excel to produce frequency diagrams for the data on the right on estimating lengths of lines.

   b The length of the line was actually 11.1 cm.
      Use your frequency diagram to write down how far out you think some of the people could have been with their guesses.

   c How good do you think people were at estimating the length of the line?
      Give your reasons.

Length estimation	
Estimate	Frequency
6.0–6.9	1
7.0–7.9	0
8.0–8.9	4
9.0–9.9	3
10.0–10.9	7
11.0–11.9	6
12.0–12.9	3
13.0–13.9	3
14.0–14.9	2
15.0–15.9	0
16.0–16.9	1

5 a Use Excel to produce frequency diagrams for the newspaper data below.

   b Use your frequency diagram to write down what you notice about the sentence length in a broadsheet newspaper.

   c Why do you think that the data is grouped?
      Give your reasons.

Newspaper sentences (broadsheet)	
Number of words	Frequency
1–5	0
6–10	2
11–15	3
16–20	3
21–25	5
26–30	4
31–35	2
36–40	1

Points to remember

⊙ You can use a spreadsheet to organise and display data.

⊙ Graphs and charts help to show features of a set of data.

⊙ The shape of the graph can also help you to interpret the data.

4 Collecting data 2

This lesson will help you to plan how to collect some data and design a questionnaire.

A **questionnaire** is a list of questions which help to collect data in a survey.

Every question on a questionnaire must have response boxes.
This is where people can answer the question, usually by putting a tick (✓) in the box.

Example 1

Joseph is finding out what kind of food people eat in a large town.
Give an example of a good question about the fruit that people eat.

Which types of fruit do you eat? (You may choose more than one.)

Apples	Bananas	Pears	Oranges	Plums	Others (please state)	Do not eat fruit
☐	☐	☐	☐	☐	☐	☐

This question is short and clear. It will help to show which types of fruit people eat.
The last two boxes make sure that everyone can fill in at least one box.

Example 2

This is an example of a poor question about the fruit that people eat.

How much do you usually spend on fruit each week?

£1 up to £3	£3 up to £5	£5 up to £10
☐	☐	☐

Explain how it could be improved.

There is no box to tick for anyone who spends less than £1 or more than £10 each week.
It could be improved by adding two more boxes 'Less than £1' and '£10 and over'.

Example 3

This is another example of a poor question about the fruit that people eat.

How often do you eat fruit?

Often	Sometimes	Now and then
☐	☐	☐

Explain how it could be improved.

The boxes could mean different things to different people. It would be better to use
'Less than once a day', 'Once or twice a day' and 'More than twice a day'.

Work in a group of three or four.

1. Your year group is going to make a visit.
   Plan a questionnaire to help you to find out what kind of visit to organise.
   Try to write questions with a good range of answers for people to choose from.

   Some questions to consider are:
   - Should the visit be on a weekday or at the weekend?
   - At what time of the year should it be?
   - Are you going on a curriculum-related visit or something else?
   - Where will you go?
   - How far are you prepared to travel?
   - How would you prefer to travel?
   - How much would you be willing to pay?

Points to remember

- Plan carefully how to collect the data needed.
- A questionnaire should have clear instructions so that people know how to answer the questions.

5 Interpreting charts and graphs

This lesson will help you to interpret graphs and charts, and say what they tell you.

The bar chart shows Rachel's and Emily's marks in four subjects.
You can tell from the chart:
- Emily scored 30 marks in art. Rachel scored 25 marks in art.
- Emily and Rachel scored the same mark in English.
- Rachel scored more marks in French.
- Emily scored 10 more marks than Rachel in science.

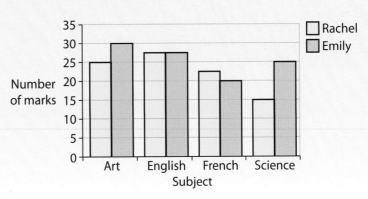

Work in a group of three or four.

You will need a copy of the results of the questionnaire on planning a year-group visit.
You will also need squared paper, glue and a large sheet of paper for a poster.

1   Produce a poster to display the findings of the questionnaire on planning a
    year-group visit.

    Discuss each question in your survey.
    Decide which graph, chart or table you need for that question and who will draw it.
    Share out the work fairly between the people in your group.

    When you have drawn your graph, chart or table, show it to the whole group
    to check that it is correct.
    Agree as a group what it shows and write this down.

    Stick your work on a large sheet of paper to show the analysis you have done for your
    survey results.

    Write some conclusions for the survey to say what you have found out about the kind of
    visit your class would like.

Points to remember

- Graphs and charts help to show features of a set of data.
- The shape of the graph can also help you to interpret the data.
- Acknowledge the source of data that you collect from the Internet or books.

How well are you doing?

Can you:

- decide what information you need to answer a question?
- plan how to collect and organise data?
- draw graphs and charts?
- interpret diagrams and graphs, and say what they tell you?

Planning and collecting data

1. *2004 level 4*

   Here is part of a questionnaire.

   a Alice is 18 years old.
      Explain why Alice cannot fill in
      this part of the questionnaire.

   b What would you would put for
      question B so that everyone can
      fill in the questionnaire?

   > **How old are you?**
   >
   > A ☐ less than 18 years old
   >
   > B ☐ more than 18 years old

Constructing and interpreting charts and diagrams

2. The table shows the results of a survey on pupils' favourite type of hobby or activity.

Hobby or activity	Frequency
Playing computer games	9
Sport	12
Reading	1
Art or craft	5
Listening to music	7
Watching television	7
Other	2

   a Use some squared paper. Draw a bar-line graph to illustrate the data.

   b Write a sentence to say what the graph shows.

3 *1999 level 5*

This graph shows the range in the temperature in Miami each month.

For example, in January the temperature ranges from 17°C to 24°C.

a In which month does Miami have the smallest range in temperature?

b In July, the range in the temperature in Miami is 5 degrees.

There are five other months in which the range in the temperature is 5 degrees.

Which five months are they?

c This graph shows the range in the temperature in Orlando each month.

In which three months is the maximum temperature in Miami greater than the maximum temperature in Orlando?

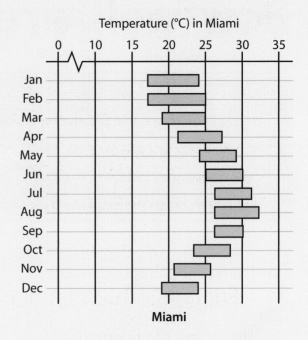

Temperature (°C) in Miami

Miami

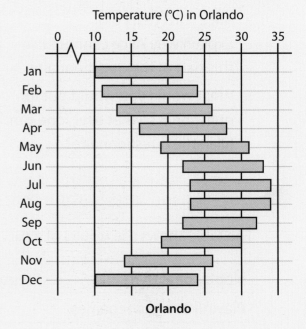

Temperature (°C) in Orlando

Orlando

4 *2006 KS2 level 5*

Class 7P did a survey of the number of trees in a country park.

This pie chart shows their results.

a Estimate the fraction of trees in the survey that are oak trees.

b The children counted 60 ash trees.

Use the pie chart to estimate the number of beech trees they counted.

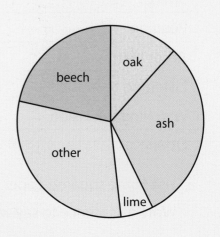

Functions and graphs

A
3.3

This unit will help you to:

- understand functions and mappings;
- read and plot coordinates;
- draw, sketch and interpret graphs;
- generate sequences using a formula for the general term.

1 Functions and mappings

This lesson will help you to write a function in words and symbols, and to draw mapping diagrams.

You can find the input of a function machine when you are given the output.

Work backwards using **inverse operations**.

$$x \rightarrow \boxed{\text{add 3}} \rightarrow y$$

$$x \leftarrow \boxed{\text{subtract 3}} \leftarrow y$$

If the output is $y = 5$, then the input is $x = 2$.

You can show a relationship between x and y in a **mapping diagram**.

The mapping diagram on the right is for the function

$$x \rightarrow \boxed{\text{multiply by 4}} \rightarrow \boxed{\text{add 2}} \rightarrow y$$

or

$$x \rightarrow 4x + 2$$

$$
\begin{aligned}
x &\rightarrow y \\
1 &\rightarrow 6 \\
2 &\rightarrow 10 \\
3 &\rightarrow 14 \\
4 &\rightarrow 18 \\
x &\rightarrow 4x + 2
\end{aligned}
$$

Exercise 1

1 Find each output y for the given input x for this function machine.

$$x \rightarrow \boxed{\text{add 11}} \rightarrow y$$

a $x = 2$ b $x = 5$ c $x = 10$ d $x = 8$

A3.3 *Functions and graphs* | **149**

② Find each output y for the given input x for this function machine.

$$x \rightarrow \boxed{\text{divide by 6}} \rightarrow y$$

a $x = 12$ b $x = 27$ c $x = 20$ d $x = 50$

③ Find each input x for the given output y for this function machine.

$$x \rightarrow \boxed{\text{add 6}} \rightarrow y$$

a $y = 7$ b $y = 11$ c $y = 13$ d $y = 21$

④ Find the outputs for each of these function machines.

a $x \rightarrow \boxed{\text{multiply by 2}} \rightarrow \boxed{\text{add 5}} \rightarrow y$ b $x \rightarrow \boxed{\text{add 5}} \rightarrow \boxed{\text{multiply by 2}} \rightarrow y$

    $x = 1, x = 2, x = 3, x = 4$ $x = 1, x = 2, x = 3, x = 4$

Are the two function machines the same?

⑤ Write the inverse function machines.

a $x \rightarrow \boxed{\text{add 4}} \rightarrow y$ b $x \rightarrow \boxed{\text{subtract 2}} \rightarrow y$

c $x \rightarrow \boxed{\text{multiply by 7}} \rightarrow y$ d $x \rightarrow \boxed{\text{divide by 6}} \rightarrow y$

e $x \rightarrow \boxed{\text{divide by 7}} \rightarrow \boxed{\text{subtract 4}} \rightarrow y$ f $x \rightarrow \boxed{\text{multiply by 5}} \rightarrow \boxed{\text{subtract 1}} \rightarrow y$

⑥ Work out the functions. Find the missing numbers in the mappings.

a $x \rightarrow y$ b $x \rightarrow y$ c $x \rightarrow y$

   $1 \rightarrow 10$ $1 \rightarrow 6$ $1 \rightarrow 4$

   $2 \rightarrow 11$ $2 \rightarrow 12$ $2 \rightarrow 9$

   $3 \rightarrow 12$ $3 \rightarrow 18$ $3 \rightarrow 14$

   $4 \rightarrow$ $4 \rightarrow$ $4 \rightarrow$

   $5 \rightarrow$ $5 \rightarrow$ $5 \rightarrow$

   $6 \rightarrow$ $6 \rightarrow$ $6 \rightarrow$

   $n \rightarrow$ $n \rightarrow$ $n \rightarrow$

The table below is another way of showing this function:

$x \rightarrow$ | multiply by 3 | $\rightarrow$ | add 1 | $\rightarrow y$

Each y number is calculated by multiplying the x number by 3 and then adding 1.

You can also write this as an equation: $y = 3x + 1$.

x	0	1	2	3	4	5
y	1	4	7	10	13	16

 Copy and complete the tables below.

a

x	1	2	3	4	5	6
$y = 5x$						

b

x	1	2	3	4	5	6
$y = 2x + 4$						

c

x	1	2	3	4	5	6
$y = 3x - 2$						

Points to remember

⊙ A function machine applies a rule or **function** to an **input** x and gives the related **output** y.

⊙ The relationship between x and y can be shown in a mapping diagram like this:

$x \rightarrow y$
$2 \rightarrow 5$
$3 \rightarrow 7$
$4 \rightarrow 9$
$x \rightarrow 2x + 1$

⊙ If the function is 'add 3', then the inverse function is 'subtract 3'.

⊙ If the function is 'multiply by 5', then the inverse function is 'divide by 5'.

2 Plotting points

This lesson will help you to read and plot points in all four quadrants.

A **coordinate pair** is an ordered pair of numbers (x, y).

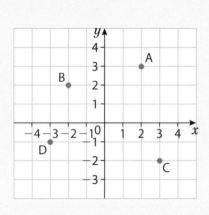

The points marked on the grid above are: A (2, 3), B (−2, 2), C (3, −2) and D (−3, −1).

Exercise 2

You will need squared paper, pencil and ruler.

1   Write the coordinates of each of the points A to J marked on the grid below.

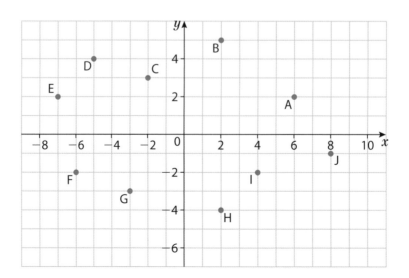

For each part of questions 2, 3 and 4, you will need to draw and label a coordinate grid.

2   **a**   Points A (-3, 0), B (1, 4) and C (5, 0) are three vertices of a square.
What are the coordinates of the fourth vertex?

   b   Points W (8, 11) and Y (3, 6) are opposite vertices of a square.
What are the coordinates of the other two vertices?

   c   Points E (1, 5) and G (1, -1) are opposite vertices of a square.
What are the coordinates of the other two vertices?

3   **a**   Points A (0, 3), B (2, 2), C (3, 0), D (2, -3) and E (0, -5) are
five vertices of an octagon.

The octagon is symmetrical about the y-axis.

The other three vertices of the octagon are F, G and H.

What are the coordinates of F, G and H?

   b   What is the area of the octagon in square units?

4   Points L (-2, -1) and M (4, -1) are two adjacent vertices of a rectangle.
The rectangle has an area of 18 square units.
What are the coordinates of the other two vertices of the rectangle?
Find two different solutions.

Extension problem

5   The points A (1, 5), B (5, 7), C (5, 3) and D (1, 1) are the vertices of parallelogram ABCD.

   a   Draw parallelogram ABCD.

   b   Plot these points:

   P, the midpoint of AB
   Q, the midpoint of BC
   R, the midpoint of CD
   S, the midpoint of AD

   c   What shape is the quadrilateral PQRS?

⊙ Points to remember

- A **coordinate pair** is an ordered pair of numbers (x, y).
- The x**-coordinate** is along the horizontal axis and the y**-coordinate** is up the vertical axis.

3 Straight-line graphs

This lesson will help you to work out the equation of a graph.

The diagram on the right shows a vertical line through the points A (2, 6), B (2, 2), C (2, −1) and D (2, −5).

The x-coordinate of all points on this line is 2.

$x = 2$ is the **equation** of the line.

The x-coordinate of all points on the y-axis is 0.

$x = 0$ is the **equation of the y-axis**.

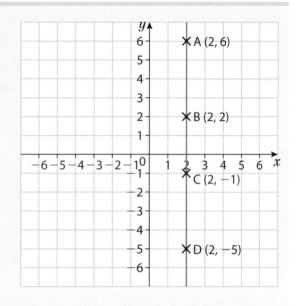

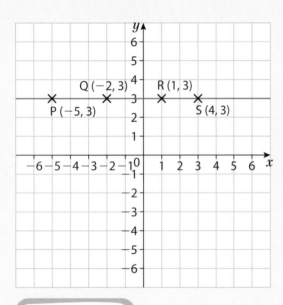

The diagram on the left shows a horizontal line through P (−5, 3), Q (−2, 3), R (1, 3) and S (4, 3).

The y-coordinate of all points on this line is 3.
The **equation** of the line is $y = 3$.
The y-coordinate of all points on the x-axis is 0.
$y = 0$ is the equation of the x-**axis**.

Exercise 3

1. The diagram shows square ABCD and rectangle PQRS.

   a Write the equation of the line:

   i AB   ii BC   iii CD   iv AD

   v QR   vi RS   vii SP   viii QP

   b For the rectangle PQRS, write the equation of:

   i the horizontal line of symmetry

   ii the vertical line of symmetry.

   c For the square ABCD, write down the equation of:

   i the horizontal line of symmetry

   ii the vertical line of symmetry.

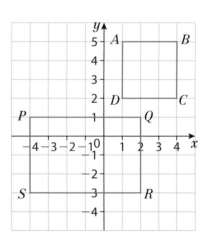

(2) Point M is (1, 3).

a Write the equation of the vertical line through M.

b Write the equation of the horizontal line through M.

(3) Point N is $(-7, -9)$.

a Write the equation of the horizontal line through N.

b Write the equation of the vertical line through N.

(4) Write the equation of the line through the points:

a (2, 1) and (2, 5)

b $(-6, 0)$ and (4, 0)

c $(-5, -3)$ and $(-5, 2)$

d $(-1, -8)$ and $(7, -8)$

Extension problem

(5) Triangle PQO has vertices at the points
P (3, 3), Q $(3, -3)$ and the origin O (0, 0).

Write the equation of:

a PQ

b the line through P parallel
to the x-axis

c the line of symmetry of triangle PQO

d OP

e OQ

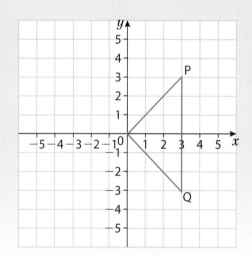

◉ Points to remember

⊙ The x-axis is the line $y = 0$; the y-axis is the line $x = 0$.

⊙ Lines parallel to the x-axis, cutting the y-axis at (0, c), have the equation
$y = c$.

⊙ Lines parallel to the y-axis, cutting the x-axis at (c, 0), have the equation
$x = c$.

⊙ You can use coordinates of points on a straight-line graph to
work out its equation.

4 Plotting straight-line graphs

This lesson will help you to draw graphs.

Did you know that...?

A **graphics calculator** can plot graphs and solve equations. Some have a colour display and some can plot 3D graphs.

The world's first graphics calculator was produced by Casio in **1985**. Hewlett Packard followed with their version soon afterwards. Texas Instruments has been making graphics calculators since 1990.

Graphics calculators are easy to program. Besides being used for maths, they are often used for games.

To draw a straight-line graph, plot three points and join them up.

Remember to continue the line to the edge of the grid.

Example

Draw the graph of $y = 2x + 1$.

Choose 3 values for x. Work out the values of y.

x	-1	0	1
$y = 2x + 1$	-1	1	3

Draw the x-axis from -5 to 5.
Draw the y-axis from -5 to 5.
Plot the coordinates $(-1, 1)$, $(0, 1)$, $(1, 3)$.
Join the points with a straight line.
Extend the line to the edges of the grid.

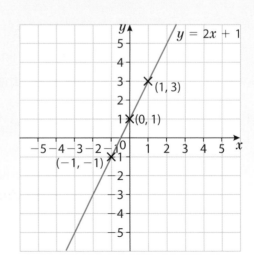

Exercise 4

You will need some squared paper.

 1 Work out three coordinate pairs that satisfy the equation.
Use them to draw the graph of the equation.

a $y = x + 3$ **b** $y = 3x + 1$ **c** $y = 2x + 5$ **d** $y = 3x - 2$

e $y = 4x + 3$ **f** $y = x + 0.5$ **g** $y = 2x - 3$ **h** $y = 5x - 4$

Extension problem

2 Work out three coordinate pairs that satisfy the equation.
Draw the graph of the equation on squared paper.

a $y = -x$ **b** $y = -2x + 1$

c $y = -x + 3$ **d** $y = -0.5x - 1$

◉ Points to remember

- ⊙ You can represent an equation like $y = 2x + 1$ as a straight-line graph.
- ⊙ To draw the graph of $y = 2x + 1$, work out the coordinates of three points. Choose three values for x and calculate the values of y.
- ⊙ There should be equal spaces between the numbers on the axes.
- ⊙ Label the grid lines, not the spaces.
- ⊙ Continue the line to the edge of the grid.
- ⊙ Every point on the line represents the the relationship $y = 2x + 1$.

5 Sequences

This lesson will help you to find a formula for the nth term of a sequence.

If you know the nth term of a sequence, you can write any term.

Example 1

The nth term of a sequence is $2n + 8$. Write the 100th term.

The 100th term is in the 100th position, so $n = 100$.
When $n = 100$, $2n + 8 = 2 \times 100 + 8 = 208$.

The differences between consecutive terms will help you to find the nth term.

Example 2

Find the nth term for the sequence:

6,   11,   16,   21,   26,   …

The difference between consecutive terms is 5.

Each term in this sequence is 'a multiple of 5, plus 1'.

The **1**st term is $5 \times \mathbf{1} + 1$.
The **2**nd term is $5 \times \mathbf{2} + 1$
The nth term is $5 \times n + 1$ or $5n + 1$

Sequences of numbers can describe patterns.

Example 3

a   Explain how the number of dots increases.

b   Draw the next two shapes in this pattern.

c   Write the number sequence that describes the pattern.

d   Write the nth term.

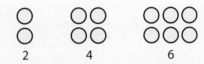

a   The pattern is made by adding two dots each time.

b   Here are the next two patterns.

c   The number sequence for the dots is 2, 4, 6, 8, 10, …

d   The nth pattern will have $2n$ dots.

Exercise 5

(1)   Write the formula for the nth term of each sequence.

a   2,   4,   6,   8,   10,   …   b   4,   8,   12,   16,   20,   …

c   10,   20,   30,   40,   …   d   6,   12,   18,   24,   30,   …

e   25,   50,   75,   100,   125, …   f   15,   30,   45,   60,   75,   …

(2)   Write the formula for the nth term of each sequence.

a   4,   7,   10,   13,   16,   …   b   3,   8,   13,   18,   23,   …

c   7,   18,   29,   40,   51,   …   d   11,   19,   27,   35,   43   …

3 For each sequence of patterns, explain how the number of dots increases.
Draw the next two shapes.
Write the first five terms of the number sequence.
Write the nth term.

a

b

c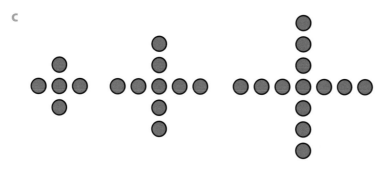

4 Here are the formulae for the nth terms of some sequences.
Write the 10th term, the 50th term and the 100th term of each sequence.

a $n + 1$ b $n - 6$ c $4n + 3$ d $3n - 7$

Extension problem

5 Here is a sequence of patterns.

a Explain how the number of dots increases.
b Draw the next two shapes.
c Write the first five terms of the number sequence.
d Write the nth term.

⊙ Points to remember

- ⊙ You can work out any term in a sequence from the **formula for the nth term.**
- ⊙ The **difference between consecutive terms** of a sequence can help you to find a formula for the nth term.
- ⊙ If the difference between consecutive terms is 3, then the nth term begins with $3n$. For example, for the sequence 1, 4, 7, 10, … the nth term is $3n - 2$.

How well are you doing?

Can you:

- read and plot coordinates in all four quadrants?
- use functions and mappings?
- draw, sketch and interpret graphs?
- generate sequences using a formula for the general term?

Functions, mappings and graphs

1 *2007 level 4*

Look at the graph.

a Write the coordinates of points A and C.

b Point D can be marked so that ABCD is a rectangle.
Write the coordinates of points D.

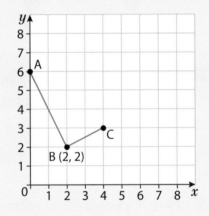

2 The diagram shows lines EF and GH.

a Write the equation of the line EF.

b Write the equation of the line GH.

The point T is (3, −2).

c Write the equation of the vertical line through T.

d Write the equation of the horizontal line through T.

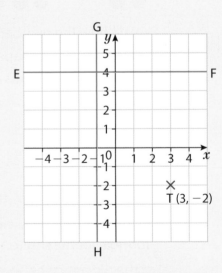

③ Copy and complete this table.

x	-2	-1	0	1	2	3
$y = 3x + 2$						

④ Work out three coordinate pairs that satisfy the equation $y = x + 5$.

Draw the graph of the equation on squared paper.

Sequences

⑤ The nth term of a sequence is $3n - 4$.

Write the first five terms of the sequence.

⑥ Look at this sequence.

1, 4, 9, 16, 25, 36, …

a Write the next three terms of the sequence.

b Write a formula for the nth term of the sequence.

Transformations

This unit will help you to:

- recognise line symmetry and rotation symmetry;
- reflect a shape in a mirror line;
- rotate a shape about a point;
- translate a shape by moving it in a straight line;
- understand that reflection, rotation and translation do not change the size or shape of an object.

1 Line symmetry

This lesson will help you to recognise line symmetry.

A shape has **line symmetry** when it can be folded so that one half of the shape fits exactly on top of the other half.

The fold line is the **line of symmetry**.

Can you see the line of symmetry in this picture?

Exercise 1

You will need **G3.3 Resource sheet 1.1**, squared paper and isometric paper.

1. Answer the question on **G3.3 Resource sheet 1.1**.

2. **a** Which of these letters do **not** have a line of symmetry?

   A B C D E F G H I J K L M
   N O P Q R S T U V W X Y Z

   b Which of the letters have two lines of symmetry?

3 Copy each pair of shapes on squared paper. Draw each line of symmetry.

a 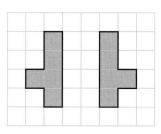   b 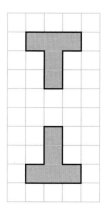   c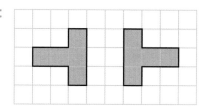

4 Draw two copies of this pattern on squared paper,

  a On one copy shade in one more square so that the pattern has two lines of symmetry.

  b On the other copy shade in three more squares so that the pattern has four lines of symmetry

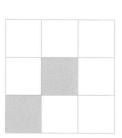

5 Copy each of these shapes on squared paper.
Colour more squares to make a pattern that is symmetrical about the mirror line.

a 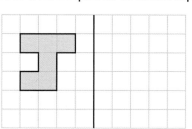   b 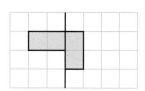   c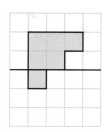

6 You need some isometric paper.

The big triangle is made from 9 small equilateral triangles.

In how many different ways can you shade three of the small triangles to make a symmetrical pattern?

One way is shown on the right.
Find the others.

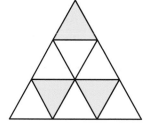

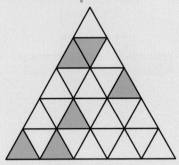

 You need some isometric paper.

The big triangle is made from 25 small
equilateral triangles.
Six of the small triangles are shaded.

What is the smallest number of extra triangles you need
to shade to make a symmetrical pattern?

8 The pentagon ABCDE is symmetrical.
What are the coordinates of point C?

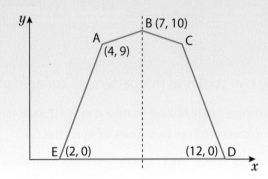

⊙ Points to remember

- ⊙ A shape has **line symmetry** when it can be folded so that one part of the
  shape fits exactly on top of the other part.
- ⊙ The fold line is the **line of symmetry**.

2 Reflections

This lesson will help you to reflect shapes in a mirror line.

When a shape is **reflected** in a **mirror line**, each point
and its reflection are the same perpendicular distance
from the mirror line.

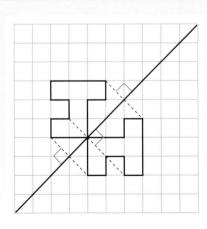

Exercise 2

You will need **G3.3 Resource sheet 2.1** and squared paper.

1 Answer the question on **G3.3 Resource sheet 2.1**.

2 Copy each shape on squared paper. Draw the mirror line.
Draw the reflection of the shape in the mirror line.

a
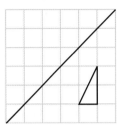

b
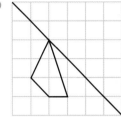

c
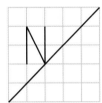

d
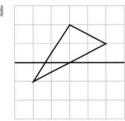

e
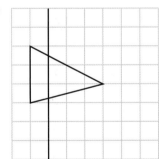

f
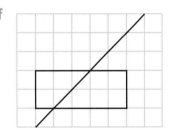

3 Each diagram shows a shape and its image after a reflection.
Copy the diagram on squared paper.
Draw the mirror line.

a
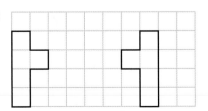

b
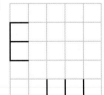

c

4 The pink triangle is a reflection of the white triangle in the mirror line.

Write the coordinates of point A and point B.

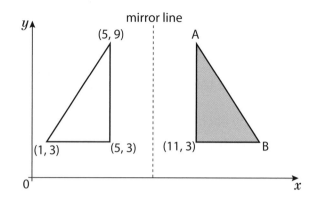

5 **a** Triangle A is reflected in the x-axis. The image is triangle B.

Write the coordinates of the three vertices of triangle B.

b Triangle A is reflected in the y-axis. The image is triangle C.

Write the coordinates of the three vertices of triangle C.

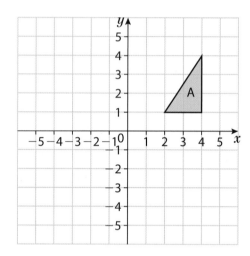

Extension problems

6 Draw axes from −5 to 5. Plot the points (−5, −5), (0, 0) and (5, 5). Join the points to make a straight line.

Now plot the points A (1, 1), B (4, 1), C (4, 3) and D (1, 3) on the grid. Join them up to make a quadrilateral ABCD.

Reflect quadrilateral ABCD in the straight line. Write down the coordinates of the image.

7 Draw axes from −5 to 5. Plot the points (5, −5), (0, 0) and (−5, 5). Join these points to make a straight line.

Now plot the points P (−1, −3), Q (0, −1), R (1, −3) and S (0, −4) on the grid. Join them up to make a quadrilateral PQRS.

Reflect quadrilateral PQRS in the straight line. Write down the coordinates of the image.

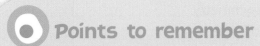

Points to remember

⊙ When a shape is reflected in a mirror line:
 – matching points of the object and image are the same perpendicular distance from the line;
 – the size and shape of the object and image are identical.

3 Rotation symmetry

This lesson will help you to recognise rotation symmetry.

A shape that fits on top of itself five times in one full turn has **rotation symmetry of order 5**. This flower has rotation symmetry of order 5.

A shape that turns one full turn before it fits onto itself has **rotation symmetry of order 1**. This triangle has rotation symmetry of order 1.

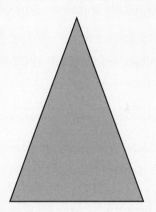

The point about which a shape is rotated is the **centre of rotation**.

Exercise 3

You will need squared paper.

① For each picture below, write down the order of rotation symmetry.

a  b  c  d

(2) A square has four lines of symmetry.
It has rotation symmetry of order 4.

Look at each of these shapes.

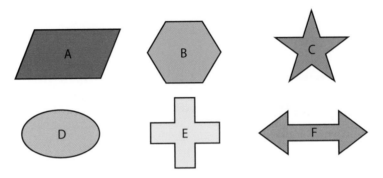

For each shape A to F, write the number of lines of symmetry and the order of rotation symmetry.

(3) a Copy this shape on squared paper.

Shade one more square so that the new shape has rotation symmetry of order 2.

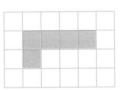

b Copy this shape on squared paper.

Shade one more square so that the new shape has rotation symmetry of order 4.

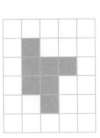

c Copy this shape on squared paper.

Shade one more square so that the new shape has rotation symmetry of order 2 and no lines of symmetry.

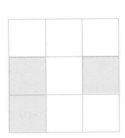

(4) For each shape, write the order of rotation symmetry.

a rectangle

b square

c rhombus

d regular octagon

e isosceles trapezium

f equilateral triangle

g parallelogram

h kite

i regular pentagon

(5) On squared paper, show how to combine these three shapes to make a single shape with rotation symmetry of order 2.

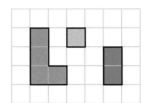

(6) Imagine rotating each letter half a turn about its centre, then reflecting it in a horizontal mirror line through its centre.

A   B   C   D   E   F   G   H   I   J   K   L   M

N   O   P   Q   R   S   T   U   V   W   X   Y   Z

a Which letters will then look the same as they did when they started?

b What do all these letters have in common?

Extension problem

(7) On squared paper, show how to combine these three shapes to make a single shape with rotation symmetry of order 4.

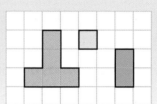

Points to remember

⊙ A shape that fits on top of itself three times in one full turn has **rotation symmetry of order 3**.

⊙ A shape that turns one full turn before it fits onto itself has **rotation symmetry of order 1**.

⊙ The point about which a shape is rotated is the **centre of rotation**.

4 Rotations

This lesson will help you to rotate a shape about a point.

Did you know that...?

All snowflakes have six lines of symmetry and rotation symmetry of order 6. But no two snowflakes are alike.

This discovery was made by a farmer **Wilson Bentley**, who lived in Jericho, a small country town in the USA.

He was famous for his photographs of snowflakes, which he took using a microscope. He was the first person ever to photograph a single snow crystal in 1885.

He became known as 'Snowflake Bentley'.

The website snowflakebentley.com/vid.htm has a video about Snowflake Bentley that you may be able to watch.

To **rotate** means to turn.

A bicycle wheel, the hands of a clock and the sails of a windmill all turn or rotate.

The pink triangle has rotated 180 degrees clockwise about the point A.

Point A is called the **centre of rotation**.

The image is the blue triangle.

The size and shape of the triangle have not changed.

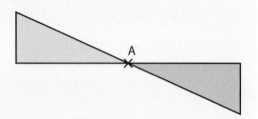

Exercise 4

You will need **G3.3 Resource sheet 4.1** and squared paper.

Answer questions 1 to 3 on **G3.3 Resource sheet 4.1**.

1　Rotate each shape 90 degrees clockwise about the point marked with a dot (•).

a　　　　　　b　　　　　　c

2 Rotate each shape 90 degrees anticlockwise about the point marked with a dot (•).

a   b   c

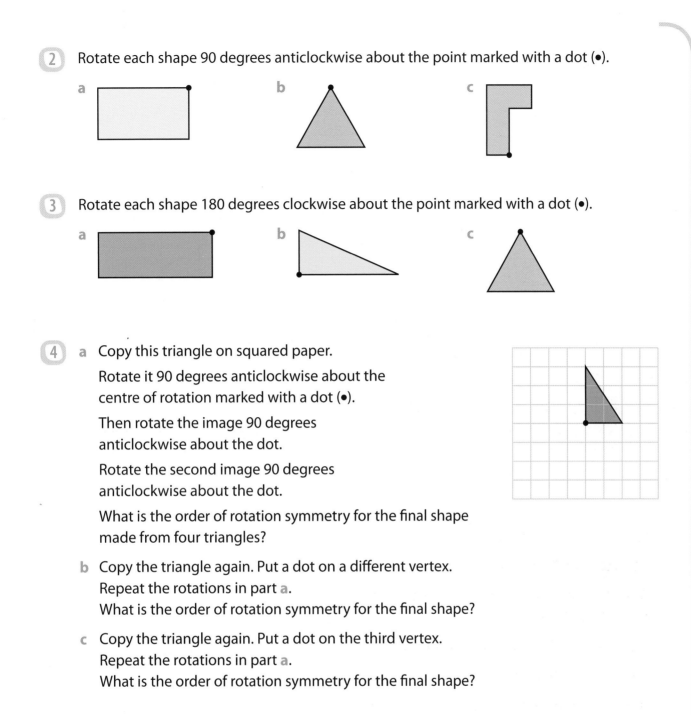

3 Rotate each shape 180 degrees clockwise about the point marked with a dot (•).

a   b   c

4   **a** Copy this triangle on squared paper.

Rotate it 90 degrees anticlockwise about the centre of rotation marked with a dot (•).

Then rotate the image 90 degrees anticlockwise about the dot.

Rotate the second image 90 degrees anticlockwise about the dot.

What is the order of rotation symmetry for the final shape made from four triangles?

b Copy the triangle again. Put a dot on a different vertex.
Repeat the rotations in part **a**.
What is the order of rotation symmetry for the final shape?

c Copy the triangle again. Put a dot on the third vertex.
Repeat the rotations in part **a**.
What is the order of rotation symmetry for the final shape?

5 Copy this rectangle on squared paper.

Rotate the rectangle about the centre of rotation (•) through:

a 90° clockwise

b 90° anticlockwise

c 180° clockwise

Label each image carefully.

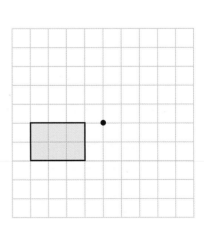

6 Copy each shape on squared paper.
Rotate the shape about the centre of rotation (•)

a 90° clockwise

b 180° clockwise

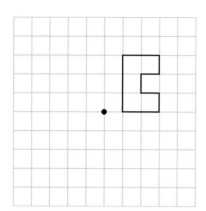

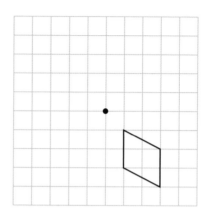

Extension problem

7 a Triangle A is rotated 90 degrees clockwise
about the origin (0, 0).
The image is triangle B.

Write the coordinates of the vertices of
triangle B.

b Triangle A is rotated 90 degrees anticlockwise
about the origin (0, 0).
The image is triangle C.

Write the coordinates of the vertices of
triangle C.

c Triangle A is rotated 180 degrees clockwise
about the origin (0, 0).
The image is triangle D.

Write the coordinates of the vertices of triangle D.

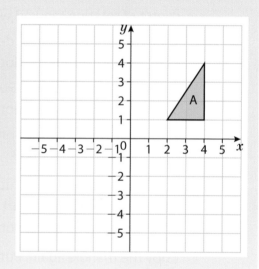

 Points to remember

⊙ When an object is rotated:
  – every point of the object turns through the same angle in the same
    direction;
  – the image is the same size and shape as the object.
⊙ The point about which a shape is rotated is the centre of rotation.

5 Translations

This lesson will help you to translate a shape by moving it in a straight line.

This diagram shows a **translation** of 4 to the right and 5 down.

The **object** is where the shape started.

The **image** is where the shape has finished after the translation.

Each point of the object has moved the same distance in the same direction.

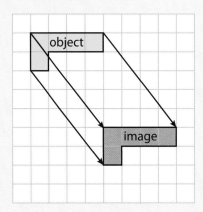

Exercise 5

1. Look at the diagram.

   Write the translation to move:

   a A to H

   b B to K

   c D to G

   d F to J

   e B to E

   f C to K

   g I to A

   h G to D

   i K to H

   j G to F

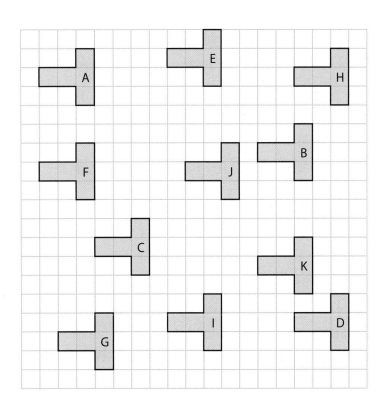

② Copy the shape on the right on squared paper.
Translate the shape:

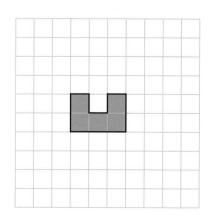

   a 2 right, 4 up. Label the image A.

   b 3 right, 2 down. Label the image B.

   c 2 left, 3 up. Label the image C.

   d 3 left, 4 down. Label the image D.

③ Write all the possible single translations of this triangle
on a 3 by 3 grid of squares.
How many are there altogether?

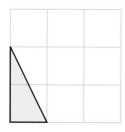

How many different single translations of the triangle
are possible on a 4 by 4 grid of squares?

How many on a 5 by 5 grid of squares?

Extension problem

④ a Triangle A is translated 4 down and 1 right.
The image is triangle B.
Write the coordinates of the vertices of triangle B.

   b Triangle A is translated 7 left and 1 up.
The image is triangle C.
Write the coordinates of the vertices of triangle C.

   c Triangle A is translated 5 left and 6 down.
The image is triangle D.
Write the coordinates of the vertices of triangle D.

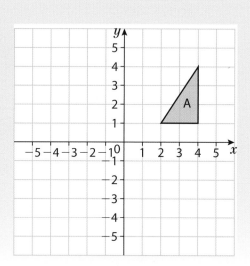

⊙ Points to remember

⊙ When an object is translated:
- every point of the object moves the same distance in the same direction;
- the image is the same size and shape as the object.

⊙ Movement to the right or left, or parallel to the x-axis, is described before
movement up or down, or parallel to the y-axis.

How well are you doing?

Can you:

- recognise line symmetry and rotation symmetry?
- reflect, rotate and translate shapes?

Symmetry

You will need squared paper.

1 *2003 level 4*

This pattern is made by shading two
3 by 1 rectangles on the grid.

The pattern has no lines of symmetry.

Copy the blank grid three times on squared paper.
On each grid, shade two 3 by 1 rectangles to make:

a a pattern with two lines of symmetry;

b a pattern with only one line of symmetry;

c a pattern with rotation symmetry of order 2.

Transformations

2 *2007 level 4*

Here is a shape.
I turn the shape through 45° clockwise.

Which diagram shows the shape after the turn?

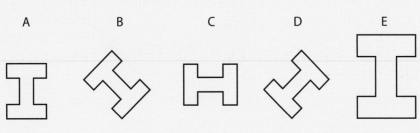

A   B   C   D   E

(3) *2006 Key Stage 2 level 4*

Copy the triangle on squared paper.
Mark point A.
The triangle is translated so that point A moves to point B.

Draw the triangle in its new position.
Use a ruler.

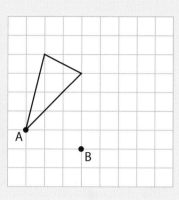

(4) *2006 level 4*

Copy the mirror lines and triangle
on squared paper.

Show the triangle reflected in the
two mirror lines.

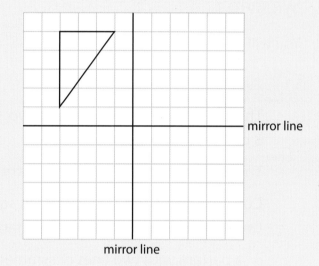

mirror line

mirror line

(5) *1997 Key Stage 2 level 6*

Copy the triangle on squared paper.

Draw the reflection of the shaded
triangle in the mirror line.

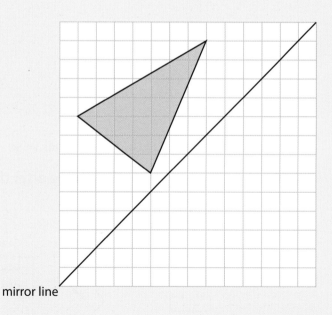

mirror line

Functional skills 2

Where is the mathematics?

This group activity will help you to:

- identify the mathematics in a situation;
- identify mathematical questions to ask about it;
- communicate your findings.

Background

Mathematics is all around us.

Looking for the maths in a situation or in information will help you to understand how widely maths is used.

Problem 1

What mathematical questions could you ask about this picture?

What answers to your questions would you give?

Problem 2

What mathematical questions could you ask about this picture?

What answers to your questions would you give?

Problem 2

What mathematical questions could you ask about this picture?

What answers to your questions would you give?

Be prepared to discuss your questions and answers with other groups.

Percentages, ratio and proportion

This unit will help you to:

- find equivalent fractions, decimals and percentages;
- work out percentages;
- divide a quantity in a given ratio;
- convert one unit to another and use conversion graphs;
- solve problems involving ratio or proportion.

1 Equivalent fractions and percentages

This lesson will help you to find equivalent fractions, decimals and percentages.

Percentage means 'per hundred', or 'in every hundred'.

Use this to change a percentage to a fraction or decimal.

Example 1   25% means 25 out of every 100, or $\frac{25}{100}$ or 0.25.
$\frac{25}{100}$ simplifies to $\frac{1}{4}$.

To change a decimal to a percentage, multiply it by 100.

Example 2   0.35 as a percentage is $0.35 \times 100\% = 35\%$.
0.4 as a percentage is $0.4 \times 100\% = 40\%$.

To change a fraction to a percentage, multiply it by 100.

Example 3 $\frac{3}{10}$ as a percentage is $\frac{3}{10}$ or $0.3 \times 100\% = 30\%$.

Exercise 1

1. Change these percentages to decimals.
   a 90%   b 6%   c 180%

2. Change these decimals to percentages.
   a 0.7   b 0.32   c 1.05

3 Change these percentages to fractions. Write each fraction in its simplest form.

a 80%   b 26%   c 15%   d 130%   e 73%   f 24%

4 Change these fractions to percentages.

a $\frac{2}{5}$ b $\frac{7}{100}$ c $\frac{2}{3}$ d $\frac{9}{25}$ e $2\frac{5}{8}$ f $1\frac{3}{40}$

5 a Emma did a survey of 100 people.
    6 of them said they were colour-blind.
    What percentage of the people asked were colour-blind?

  b Rory had 25 sweets.
    He ate 13 of them.
    What percentage of his sweets did Rory eat?

  c There are 500 pupils in a school.
    220 of them are boys.
    What percentage of the pupils are girls?

  d In a survey of 250 people, 210 of them said that they
    liked cheese.
    What percentage of people did not like cheese?

  e 56 children are playing in a playground.
    21 of them are girls.
    What percentage are boys?

  f 96 people were asked if they liked pop music.
    52 said yes. 28 said no. The rest said that they did not know.
    What percentage of the people asked did not know?

6 Find a partner to play **Four in a row**.
You will need **N3.5 Resource sheet 1.1**,
some small counters in two colours, and a calculator.

Rules

Choose which percentage of 800 gives an answer
on the board.
The full set of rules is on the resource sheet.

200	656	288	792	136	496
408	128	528	96	664	224
600	240	440	608	160	400
80	720	192	256	544	104
512	272	480	144	616	648
320	120	640	560	392	208

Points to remember

⊙ To change a fraction or a decimal to a percentage, multiply it by 100.

⊙ Use percentages to compare proportions.

2 Finding percentages, including discounts

This lesson will help you to calculate and solve problems involving percentages.

	Examples
To find **50%** of a number or quantity, halve it.	**50%** of £30 is $\frac{1}{2}$ of £30 = £15
To find **25%**, find half of 50%.	**25%** of £30 is $\frac{1}{2}$ of £15 = £7.50
To find **75%**, add 50% and 25%.	**75%** of £30 = 50% of £30 + 25% of £30
	$\qquad\qquad$ = £15 + £7.50 = £22.50
To find **10%**, divide the number or quantity by 10.	**10%** of £30 is $\frac{1}{10}$ of £30 = £3
To find **5%**, find 10% and then halve it.	**5%** of £30 is $\frac{1}{2}$ of £3 = £1.50
To find **15%**, find 10%, then add 5%.	**15%** of £30 = 10% of £30 + 5% of £30
	$\qquad\qquad$ = £3 + £1.50 = £4.50

Exercise 2

1. What percentage of each shape is shaded?

    a   **b**   **c**   **d**

    e 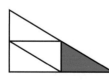   **f**   **g**   **h**

2. For each circle, estimate the percentage that is shaded blue.

    a 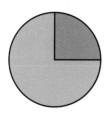   **b** 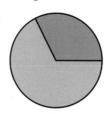   **c**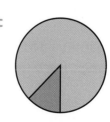

    d 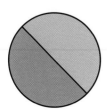   **e** 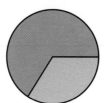   **f**

(3) **Without using a calculator**, write the answers to these calculations.

a 50% of 62 g   b 25% of 240 m   c 75% of 500 kg   d 10% of 44 cm

e 5% of 500 ml   f 35% of £600   g 20% of 80 litres   h 60% of £250

(4) Julie carried out a survey.

She asked people if they were frightened of spiders.
She used her calculator.
64.10256% of those she asked said yes.

There were 39 people in Julie's survey.
How many of them said they were frightened of spiders?

⦿ Points to remember

⊙ A quick way to find 20% of a quantity is to find 10% by dividing by 10, then multiply this by 2 to find 20%. You can find 30%, 40%, 50%, … similarly.

⊙ If there is no quick method for finding a percentage of a quantity, first find 1%, then multiply this by the value of the percentage.

⊙ Always include any units in the answer.

3 Dividing a quantity in a given ratio

This lesson will help you to solve problems involving ratios.

Simplify ratios like fractions by dividing each side by the same number.

Example 1   Simplify the ratio 5 : 10.

Divide both sides of the ratio 5 : 10 by 5 to get 1 : 2.

To divide a quantity into two parts in the ratio $a:b$, begin by dividing the quantity into $a + b$ equal units. Put a units in one part, and b units in the other part.

Example 2   Divide £160 in the ratio 3 : 5.

There are 3 + 5 = 8 equal units.
One unit is £160 ÷ 8 = £20.
So 3 units are £20 × 3 = £60.
5 units are £20 × 5 = £100.

Answer: £60 : £100

1. Divide £100 in each of these ratios.

   a 1:9   b 1:3   c 2:3

   d 3:7   e 9:11   f 9:16

2. There are 250 children in a primary school.
   The ratio of boys to girls is 3:2. How many boys are there?

3. Rosie has 24 pencils in a box.
   The ratio of red pencils to blue pencils is 5:1.
   How many of each type of pencil does she have?

4. Leroy collects CDs.
   He now has 120 CDs.
   The ratio of pop music to jazz is 5:7.
   How many of each type of CD does
   Leroy have?

5. Asif has saved 36 coins.
   They are all £1 coins or 50p coins.
   The ratio of £1 coins to 50p coins is 1:3.
   How much money has Asif saved?

6. Tess made 350 ml of orange drink.
   She mixed orange squash with water in the ratio 1:4.
   How many millilitres of water did Tess use?

7. Mrs Khan has a vegetable plot with an area of 15 m².
   She divided the plot into two rectangles in the ratio 1:2.
   What is the area of the larger rectangle?

8. A 5 litre tin of orange paint has been made.
   Red paint and yellow paint have been mixed in the ratio 7:3.
   How many litres of red paint have been used?

9. Rebecca stuck 16 stamps on a large parcel.
   They are all 25p or 35p stamps.
   The ratio of 25p stamps to 35p stamps is 3:5.
   What is the total value of the stamps on the parcel?

10 Use your ruler to draw a line AB 75 mm long.

Mark a point P so that AP to PB is in the ratio 2:3.

Write the lengths of AP and PB in millimetres on your line.

11 Use your ruler and protractor to draw an angle ABC of 80°.

Divide ABC into two smaller angles ABX and XBC in the ratio 3:5.

Write the sizes of angles ABX and XBC on your diagram.

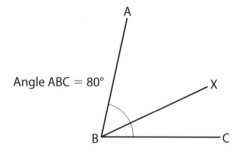

Angle ABC = 80°

Extension problem

12 Jamie is mixing fruit punch for a party.

He has a 5 litre container of cranberry juice and 3 litres of pineapple juice in a similar container.

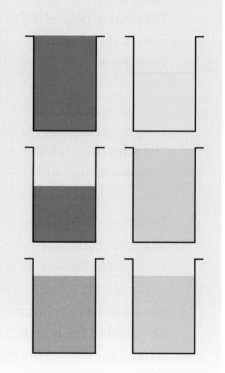

He pours 2 litres of cranberry juice into the other container and mixes them well.

He then pours 1 litre of the mixture back into the cranberry juice and mixes them well.

a How much juice is in the first container now?

b How much of this is cranberry juice?

c How much is pineapple juice?

Points to remember

⊙ To divide a quantity into two parts in the ratio $a:b$:

– first divide the quantity into $a + b$ equal units;

– then put a units in one part, and b units in the other part.

4 Direct proportion

This lesson will help you to solve problems involving proportion.

To solve direct proportion problems:

- ☺ make sure that the units are the same for each variable;
- ☺ use a four-cell diagram;
- ☺ try to arrange the diagram so that the unknown is in the bottom right corner;
- ☺ look for a relationship — it can be from left to right or top to bottom;
- ☺ apply the same relationship to the other variable to find the unknown number.

Example

Cream cheese costs £3.60 for 1 kg. Jack buys a pot of cream cheese for 90p.
How many grams of cream cheese does he buy?

cost (p)	cheese (g)
360	1000
90	?

÷ 4

Answer: Jack buys 1000 g ÷ 4 = 250 g of cream cheese.

Exercise 4

1. 6 packets of crisps cost £1.80. How much do 10 packets of crisps cost?

2. 5 pens cost £5.50. How much do 9 pens cost?

3. Patrick can run 10 km in 40 minutes.
   At the same rate, how long does he take
   to run 12 km?

4. Amy earns £42 in 6 hours.
   How much would she earn in 5 hours?

5. In 2 days my watch gains 10 seconds.
   How much time does it gain in a week?

6. 3 kg of flour costs £1.80.
   How much does 4 kg flour cost?

7 10 books on a shelf take up 30 cm of shelf space.
How much shelf space is needed for 27 books.

8 25 metres of curtain material cost £75.
What do 15 metres of the material cost?

9 In 5 days, Stephanie drinks 7.5 litres of water.
How much water does she drink in one week?

10 A sheet of 15 postage stamps costs £45.
How many of the same stamps can you buy for £21?

Extension problem

 Did you know that...?

A **sundial** uses a shape called a gnomon to cast a shadow on a set of marks for each hour.

The marks depend on the location of the sundial, since the height of the sun in the sky and the length and angle of shadows is different in different places.

The oldest sundial in Rome was stolen from Sicily in 264 BC. It had the wrong marks for Rome and it gave the wrong time for over 100 years!

The world's biggest sundial is currently the mast of Sundial Bridge at Turtle Bay in California.

Sundial Bridge, California

The shadow is cast on a large dial to the north of the bridge, but it is exactly accurate on only one day a year, 21 June.

11 Zak's watch is so accurate that it gains only 1 second an hour.
He last corrected it at midnight on 31 December 2008 ready for the New Year.
If he does not alter it again, when will it next be correct?

Points to remember

⊙ Use a diagram to help you solve direct proportion problems.
  – Make sure that the units are the same for each variable.
  – Try to put the unknown in the bottom right corner.
⊙ Look for a relationship. It can be from left to right or top to bottom.
⊙ Use the relationship to find the unknown number.

5 Conversion graphs

This lesson will help you to convert one unit to another and to use conversion graphs.

Use the relationship between two units to convert from one unit to another.

Example 1

4 litres is roughly the same as 7 pints. Roughly how many pints is 12 litres?

You multiply 4 litres by 3 to get 12 litres. So multiply 7 pints by 3 to get 21 pints.

Answer: 21 pints

You can use a **conversion graph** to convert one unit to another.

Example 2

This graph shows how to convert Swiss francs into pounds (£).

How many pounds do you get for 20 Swiss francs?

Find 20 francs on the horizontal scale of the graph.
Follow the green line to the graph.
Read off the number of £ from the vertical scale.

Answer: £2.50

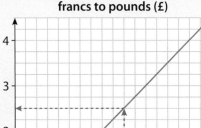
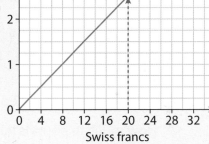

Conversion graph: Swiss francs to pounds (£)

Exercise 5

1. A mass of 2 pounds is roughly the same as 1 kilogram.
   a Roughly how many pounds is 19 kilograms?
   b Roughly how many kilograms is 32 pounds?
   c A stone is 14 pounds. John weighs 10 stone. About how many kilograms is this?

2. 4 litres is roughly the same as 7 pints.
   a Roughly how many litres is 28 pints?
   b Roughly how many pints is 24 litres?
   c A gallon is 8 pints. Raj used 14 gallons of water for a bath. About how many litres is this?

3. One pound (£) is worth roughly 1.5 euros.
   a Roughly how much is £30 worth in euros?
   b Roughly how much is 12 euros worth in pounds (£)?

4　This graph converts kilograms (kg) into pounds (lb).

Conversion graph: kilograms to pounds

pounds (lb)

[Graph showing a straight line from origin, with pounds (lb) on the vertical axis marked at 4, 8, 12, 16, 20, 24, 28, 32, 36 and kilograms (kg) on the horizontal axis marked at 0, 2, 4, 6, 8, 10, 12, 14, 16]

kilograms (kg)

a　Convert 13 kilograms into pounds.

b　Convert 25 pounds into kilograms.

c　A large bag of potatoes weighs 5 kg. About how many pounds is this?

d　A bag of carrots weighs 6 pounds. About how many kilograms is this?

e　A bag of sugar weighs 1 kg. Roughly how many pounds is this?

5　One pound (£) is worth about 1.5 euros.

a　How much in pounds (£) do you need to change to get 57 euros?

b　Alice changes £50 into euros. She spends 48 euros on holiday in France. After her holiday, she changes the euros back into pounds. About how much does she get in pounds?

Points to remember

⊙ Conversion graphs are always straight lines.

⊙ To draw a conversion graph, plot at least two points.

⊙ You may need to estimate a reading from a conversion graph.

How well are you doing?

Can you:

- find equivalent fractions, decimals and percentages;

- work out percentages;

- divide a quantity in a given ratio;

- solve problems involving ratio or proportion?

Percentages, ratio and proportion (no calculator)

1 On a school visit, one teacher must go with every 20 pupils.

   a 105 pupils go on a school visit. 63 of the pupils are girls.
What percentage of the pupils are girls?

   b Three teachers go on a school visit.
What is the greatest number of pupils they can take with them?

   c The table below shows how many pupils go on three school visits.

    Copy and complete the table to show the lowest number of teachers
that must go with each school trip.

Number of pupils	Number of teachers
100	
106	
197	

2 *Y7 Optional Test level 5*

A 500 g packet of Tasty cereal contains fruit and cereal.
40% of it is fruit. 60% is cereal.

   a How many grams of fruit does this packet of Tasty contain?

   b How many 60 gram servings can you get from one

  - packet of Tasty?

   c The ratio of fruit to cereal in a packet of Tasty is 40 : 60.
Write this ratio in its simplest form.

3 *1999 level 5*

    a Nigel pours 1 carton of apple juice and 3 cartons of orange juice into a big jug. What is the ratio of apple juice to orange juice in Nigel's jug?

    b Lesley pours 1 carton of apple juice and $1\frac{1}{2}$ cartons of orange juice into another big jug. What is the ratio of apple juice to orange juice in Lesley's jug?

    c Tandi pours 1 carton of apple juice and 1 carton of orange juice into another big jug.
    She wants only half as much apple juice as orange juice in her jug.
    What should Tandi pour into her jug now?

4 *1998 level 5*

You can make different colours of paint by mixing red, blue and yellow in different proportions. For example, you can make green paint by mixing 1 part blue paint to 1 part yellow paint.

    a To make purple, you mix 3 parts red to 7 parts blue.
    How much of each colour do you need to make 20 litres of purple paint?
    Give your answer in litres.

    b To make orange, you mix 12 parts yellow to 8 parts red.
    How much of each colour do you need to make 10 litres of orange paint?
    Give your answer in litres.

5 Mike takes 32 minutes to jog 8 km.
At the same rate, how long does he take to jog 6 km?

6 Free-range eggs cost £1.20 for 6.
How many eggs can you buy for £6?

Properties of shapes

This unit will help you to:

- identify perpendicular and parallel lines;
- recognise and use properties of triangles and quadrilaterals;
- know and use the angle sum of a triangle;
- work out unknown angles in diagrams;
- solve problems by breaking them into steps.

1 Parallel and perpendicular lines

This lesson will help you to identify perpendicular and parallel lines.

Two lines are **perpendicular** if the angle between them is a right angle.

Lines are **parallel** if they are always the same distance apart. Parallel lines never meet, even when they are extended.

The vertical railings are parallel. The horizontal railings are also parallel.

The horizontal and vertical railings are at right angles to each other, so they are perpendicular.

In diagrams, arrows are used to show that lines are parallel.

Exercise 1

You will need a ruler, protractor or set square and a sharp pencil.

1. For each pair of lines, write whether they are parallel, perpendicular or neither.

   a  b  c  d

2
a Name the right angle in two different ways.
b Name the vertical side.

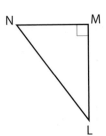

3
a Copy the trapezium.
Mark with arrows a pair of parallel lines.
b What type of angle is angle x?

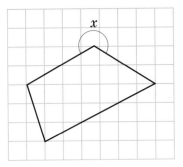

4
a Which is the acute angle?
b Name the pair of parallel sides.
c Which side is perpendicular to EF?

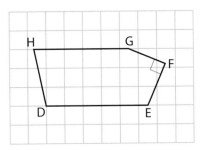

5 Look at these three rectangles.

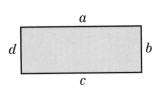 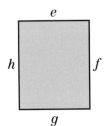 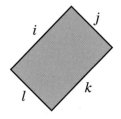

a Write six pairs of sides that are parallel.
b Which sides are perpendicular to side a?
c Which sides are perpendicular to side d?
d Which sides are perpendicular to side f?
e Which sides are perpendicular to side k?

6 Draw a pair of parallel lines at a perpendicular distance apart of 5 cm.

7 Make an accurate drawing of:
a a square with sides 5.8 cm
b a rectangle with length 7.6 cm and width 5.3 cm.

8 Make an accurate drawing of:

a this right-angled triangle

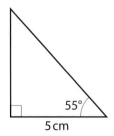

55°

5 cm

b this rhombus

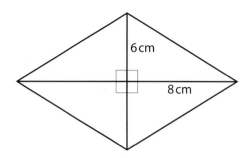

6 cm

8 cm

Points to remember

⊙ **Parallel lines** are always the same distance apart.

⊙ Parallel lines never meet even if they are extended.

⊙ **Perpendicular lines** meet or cross each other at right angles.

⊙ On diagrams, parallel lines are marked with arrows and perpendicular lines with a right angle.

---

2 Properties of shapes 1

This lesson will help you to remember some properties of triangles and quadrilaterals.

Some **triangles** have special properties.

Right-angled triangle
one right angle

Acute-angled triangle
three acute angles

Obtuse-angled triangle
one obtuse and two acute angles

Isosceles triangle
two equal sides
two equal angles
one line of symmetry
no rotation symmetry

Equilateral triangle
three equal sides
three equal angles
three lines of symmetry
rotation symmetry of order 3

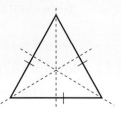

Some **quadrilaterals** have special properties.

Square
all sides equal in length
opposite sides parallel
all angles are 90°

Rectangle
opposite sides equal in length
opposite sides parallel
all angles are 90°

Parallelogram
opposite sides equal in length
opposite sides parallel
opposite angles equal

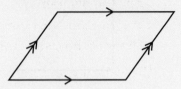

Rhombus
all sides equal in length
opposite sides parallel
opposite angles equal

Trapezium
one pair of parallel sides

Isosceles trapezium
one pair of parallel sides
non-parallel sides equal in length

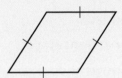
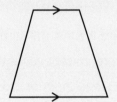
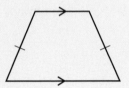

Kite
two pairs of adjacent sides equal in length
one pair of opposite angles equal
('adjacent' means 'next to')

Arrow head
two pairs of adjacent sides equal in length
one pair of opposite angles equal
one reflex angle

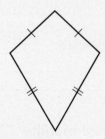
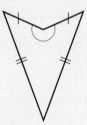

Exercise 2

1. Two of the quadrilaterals described above do not have any lines of symmetry.
   Write their names.

2. Four of the quadrilaterals described above do not have rotation symmetry.
   Write their names.

3. Sketch each of these quadrilaterals. Draw all the lines of symmetry.
   Write how many lines of symmetry each shape has.

   a rectangle   b kite   c square

   d rhombus   e isosceles trapezium

4 Write the order of rotation symmetry of:

    a a square   **b** a rectangle   **c** a parallelogram   **d** a rhombus

5 The diagram shows an arrowhead.

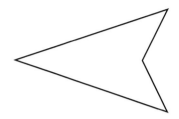

    a Copy the diagram.
       On your diagram, mark clearly any pairs
       of lines of the same length.

    b Draw the line of symmetry.

    c Does an arrowhead have rotation symmetry?

6 **a** On squared paper, draw a right-angled triangle that has one line of symmetry.
       Draw the line of symmetry on your triangle.

    b Write down what is special about this right-angled triangle.

Extension problems

A **regular polygon** is a polygon with all its sides the same length and all its angles equal.

An **equilateral triangle** is a regular polygon with three sides.
It has three lines of symmetry and rotation symmetry of order 3.

A **square** is a regular polygon with four sides.
It has four lines of symmetry and rotation symmetry of order 4.
Here are some more regular polygons.

Pentagon	**Hexagon**	**Heptagon**	**Octagon**	**Decagon**
5 equal sides	6 equal sides	7 equal sides	8 equal sides	10 equal sides
5 equal angles	6 equal angles	7 equal angles	8 equal angles	10 equal angles

7 Write the number of lines of symmetry of:

    a a regular pentagon   **b** a regular hexagon   **c** a regular octagon

8 Write the order of rotation symmetry of:

    a a regular pentagon   **b** a regular hexagon   **c** a regular octagon

9 For a regular polygon, what is the link between the number of its sides, the number of its lines of symmetry and its order of rotation symmetry?

10 A regular polygon has 15 lines of symmetry.

    a How many sides has this polygon?

    b What is its order of rotation symmetry?

⦿ Points to remember

- ⊙ A **right-angled triangle** has one angle of 90°.
- ⊙ An **isosceles triangle** has two equal sides and two equal angles.
  It has one line of symmetry.
- ⊙ An **equilateral triangle** has three equal sides and three equal angles.
  It has three lines of symmetry and rotation symmetry of order 3.
- ⊙ A **quadrilateral** has four sides. Some special quadrilaterals are the square, rectangle, parallelogram, rhombus, kite, arrowhead, trapezium.

3 Properties of shapes 2

This lesson will help you to use the properties of shapes to solve problems.

Exercise 3

Work in pairs. You will need **G3.4 Resource sheet 3.1**, a ruler and a protractor.

1 Draw the diagonals of each quadrilateral on the resource sheet. Use a ruler.
Measure the lengths of the diagonals to the nearest millimetre.
Measure the angle where the diagonals intersect to the nearest degree.

Copy this table. Write the name of each quadrilateral in the correct box.

Diagonals	Equal in length	Not equal in length
Perpendicular		
Not perpendicular		

- The diagonals of a square, rhombus, kite and arrowhead cross each other at right angles.
- The diagonals of a square, rectangle, parallelogram and rhombus cut each other in half.
- The properties of shapes can be used to solve problems.

4 Investigating shapes

This lesson will help you to investigate the properties of shapes.

Exercise 4

You will need square dotty paper.

 1 You can make shapes on pinboards by joining pins.

Here are a triangle and a pentagon made on pinboard.
Each shape has a pin at each corner.

Using 3 by 3 pinboard, how many different quadrilaterals can you make? Each quadrilateral must have a pin at each corner.

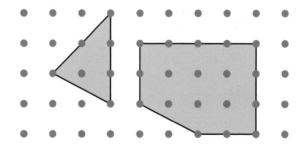

Use square dotty paper to record your results.
By each different shape that you make, write what kind of quadrilateral it is.

Extension problem

2 How many triangles are there in each diagram?

a

b

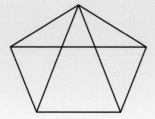

Points to remember

- Triangles with special properties are an **equilateral triangle**, an **isosceles triangle** and **right-angled triangle**.
- A triangle in which all three sides are different lengths is called a **scalene triangle**.
- Scalene triangles can be **acute-angled** or **obtuse-angled**.
- A quadrilateral has four sides. Some special quadrilaterals are the **square**, **rectangle**, **parallelogram**, **rhombus**, **kite**, **arrowhead** and **trapezium**.

5 Angle sum of a triangle

This lesson will help you to find and use the angle sum of a triangle.

Draw a triangle.
Label its angles a, b and c.

Tear off its corners.

Fit angles a, b and c together.
They make a straight line.

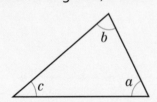
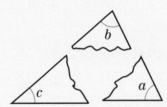
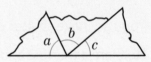

The angles on a straight line add up to 180° and so the angles in this triangle add up to 180°.

Example

Find the size of the angle marked x.

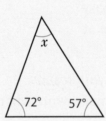

$72° + 57° = 129°$
$180° - 129° = 51°$
$x = 51°$

Exercise 5

1 Find the size of each angle marked with a letter.
Give your reasons.

a
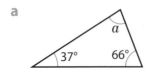

b
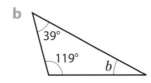

c
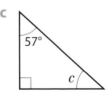

2 Find the size of each angle marked with a letter.
Give your reasons.

a
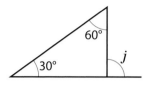

b
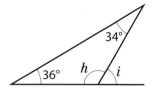

c
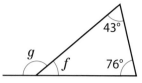

d
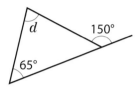

e
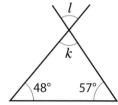

f
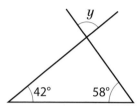

g
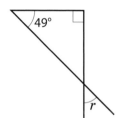

h
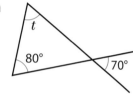

i
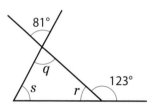

3 Helen measures the angles of a triangle.

She says: 'The angles of this triangle are 30°, 50° and 110°.'
Is Helen correct?

Write **Yes** or **No**. Give your reasons.

An **isosceles triangle** has two equal sides and two equal angles.

An **equilateral triangle** has three equal sides and three equal angles.

4 Find the size of each angle marked with a letter.
Give your reasons.

a
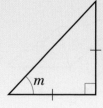

b
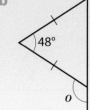

c
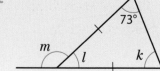

5 The diagram shows an isosceles triangle.

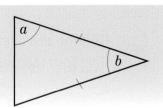

   a When angle b is 76°, what is the size of angle a?

   b When angle a is 76°, what is the size of angle b?

 Points to remember

⊙ Angles in a triangle sum to 180°.

⊙ You can use this property to solve problems.

⊙ Never measure an angle that you are asked to find or calculate.

6 Solving problems

This lesson will help you to use the properties of angles and triangles to solve problems.

 Did you know that...?

Hypatia was born in Alexandria about 370 AD.

Her father taught her maths and she later became the head of the school where she taught.

She was a lively teacher and also beautiful and modest. She rewrote earlier maths books to make them easier for her pupils to study, including some books on geometry written by **Euclid**.

Hypatia was the first woman to make a major contribution to mathematics. She was murdered when she was 45 years old by a fanatical Christian sect who did not like her views on learning.

Exercise 6

Draw a quadrilateral.
Label its angles a, b, c and d.

Tear off its corners.

Fit angles a, b, c and d together.
They make a point.

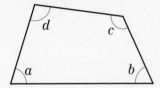

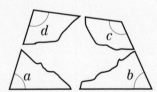

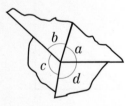

The angles on a straight line add up to 180° and so the angles in this triangle add up to 180°.

Example

Find the size of the angle marked x.

$76° + 118° + 98° = 292°$

$360° - 292° = 68°$

$x = 68°$

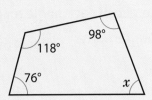

---

(1) Find the size of each angle marked with a letter.
Give your reasons.

a
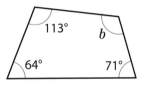

b
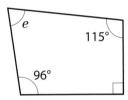

c
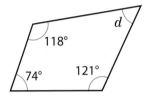

d
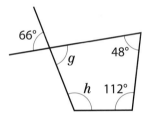

e
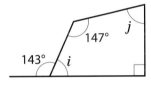

f
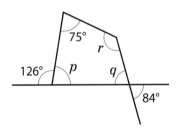

(2) **a** The diagram shows an isosceles trapezium.
Find the size of each angle marked with a letter.
Give your reasons.

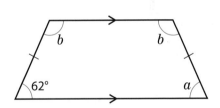

b The diagram shows a kite.
Find the size of each angle marked with a letter.
Give your reasons.

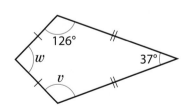

c The diagram shows a rectangle.
Find the size of each angle marked with a letter.
Give your reasons.

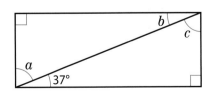

3　**a** The diagram shows a kite.

Find the size of each angle marked with a letter.

Give your reasons.

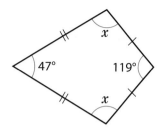

b The diagram shows a parallelogram.

Find the size of each angle marked with a letter.

Give your reasons.

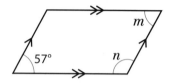

c The diagram shows an arrowhead.

Find the size of each angle marked with a letter.

Give your reasons.

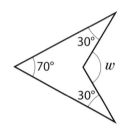

Extension problem

 ABC is an equilateral triangle.

Find angle ADB, angle BAD and angle DAC.

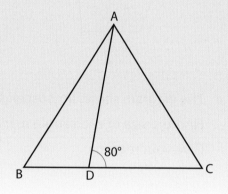

Points to remember

⊙ Draw a neat diagram.

⊙ Add information you are given to your diagram.

⊙ Break the problem into steps.

⊙ Use the properties of angles and shapes.

⊙ When you write your solution, always give your reasons.

How well are you doing?

Can you:

- identify perpendicular and parallel lines?

- recognise and use properties of triangles and quadrilaterals?

- know and use the angle sum of a triangle and of a quadrilateral?

- work out unknown angles in diagrams?

- solve problems by breaking them into steps?

You will need squared paper.

Properties of 2D shapes

1 *2006 level 4*

Look at the shaded shape on the square grid.
For each statement below, write **True** or **False**.

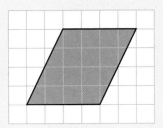

a The shaded shape is a quadrilateral.

b The shaded shape has four equal sides.

c The shaded shape has four equal angles.

d The shaded shape has two pairs of parallel sides.

2 *2007 level 4*

Sam says:

> The **only** four-sided shape with four right angles is a square.

Is Sam correct? Write **Yes** or **No**.
Explain your answer.

3 *2007 level 5*

a A triangle has three equal sides.
Write the sizes of the angles in this triangle.

b A right-angled triangle has two equal sides.
Write the sizes of the angles in this triangle.

Where could you put point E so that shape
ABCDE is a trapezium?

Write the coordinates.

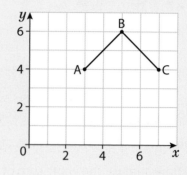

⑤ Look at this diagram.

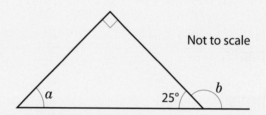

Not to scale

Calculate the size of angle a and angle b.

⑥ *2004 level 5*

On squared paper, draw a quadrilateral that has exactly two right angles.

Enquiry 2

This unit will help you to:

- investigate problems by collecting and using data;
- decide what information you need and where to find it;
- plan how to collect and organise data, and design a collection sheet;
- draw graphs and charts on paper or using ICT;
- find simple statistics and use them to compare sets of information;
- interpret statistics, graphs and chart, and say what they tell you;
- write a short report of an investigation.

1 Collecting data

This lesson will help you to plan how to collect and organise some data, and design a collection sheet.

When you design a data collection sheet you need:
- a row for each person you collect data from or each item that you count;
- a column for each question you ask or each piece of data you record.

Make the columns and rows big enough to write the information in.

Example

Mark is doing a traffic survey for the local council.

He wants to know what kinds of vehicles are using a stretch of road during the rush hour.

Design a data collection sheet for him.

Number	Colour	Type of vehicle	Number of people in vehicle
1	Blue	Car	2
2	Red	Van	1
3	Silver	Car	3
4	White	Lorry	1
5			

Fruit and vegetables

⊙ What proportion of people eat the recommended five portions of fruit and vegetables a day?

⊙ Do older people eat more fruit and vegetables than younger people?

⊙ Do females eat more fruit and vegetables than males?

Work with a partner.

Design a data collection sheet to find the information needed to answer the questions above.

Think about:

⊙ the data you need to collect from each person;

⊙ the number of pieces of information you need to collect;

⊙ the kinds of answers people will give you.

The table should have rows for at least ten people to answer the survey.

Points to remember

⊙ When you plan a survey it helps to think about the **data handling cycle**.

⊙ A **data collection sheet** is a table for recording survey results.

⊙ When you plan your data collection sheet, think about the answers people may give.

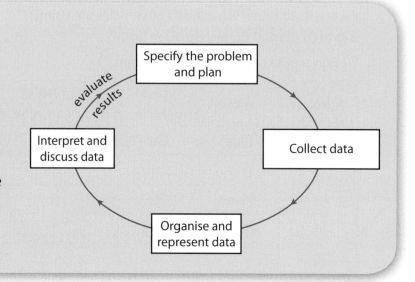

2 Calculating statistics

This lesson will help you to calculate simple statistics for small sets of data.

- The **range** is the difference between the largest and smallest numbers in a set. It is a measure of how spread out the numbers are.

The mean, median and mode are different ways of finding the **average** of a set of numbers.

- The **mean** is found by adding up all the numbers in the set and dividing by the number of numbers in the set.
- The **median** is the middle number, or the mean of the middle two numbers, when all the numbers in the set are arranged in order.
- The **mode** is the number that occurs most often in the set. For grouped data, the **modal class** is the group that occurs most often.

Example 1

Elise spins a spinner 12 times and gets these results:

   1,   3,   3,   4,   4,   2,   4,   3,   2,   2,   4,   4

Find the range and the mode, mean and median.

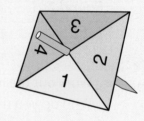

Range = 4 − 1 = 3

Mode = 4

Mean = (1 + 3 + 3 + 4 + 4 + 2 + 4 + 3 + 2 + 2 + 4 + 4) ÷ 12 = 36 ÷ 12 = 3

Median: The scores in order are 1, 2, 2, 2, 3, 3, 3, 4, 4, 4, 4, 4.
The middle pair is 3, 3 so the median is 3.

Example 2

The mean of the seven numbers on the cards is 4.
Find some pairs of values for the two mystery numbers.

All seven numbers must add to 4 × 7 = 28.

2 + 3 + 4 + 4 + 7 = 20 so the remaining two numbers must add to 8.

Possible pairs of values are 1 and 7, 2 and 6, 3 and 5, and 4 and 4.

Check that these values work:

2 + 3 + 4 + 4 + 7 + 1 + 7 = 28, so the mean is 28 ÷ 7 = 4
2 + 3 + 4 + 4 + 7 + 2 + 6 = 28, so the mean is 28 ÷ 7 = 4
2 + 3 + 4 + 4 + 7 + 3 + 5 = 28, so the mean is 28 ÷ 7 = 4
2 + 3 + 4 + 4 + 7 + 4 + 4 = 28, so the mean is 28 ÷ 7 = 4

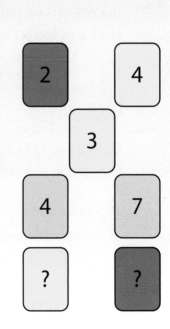

① The mean of five numbers is 6. Four of the numbers are 4, 6, 7, and 8.

  a What is the total of the five numbers?

  b What is the fifth number?

② Six numbers have a mean of 7 and a range of 10.
   Four of the numbers are 2, 7, 8 and 11.
   What are the other two numbers?

③ The mean of five numbers is 5 and the median is 4.
   Three of the numbers are 2, 3 and 8.
   What are the other two?

④ Meena went bowling with her friends Erin and Freya. The table shows their scores.

	Meena	Erin	Freya
Round 1	112	79	121
Round 2	85	101	60
Round 3	105	85	98

  a Work out the mean and range for each player.
    Who do you think is the best player and why?

  b Meena thinks that Freya is the best player.
    Is she right?

⑤ The friends then decided that the winner would be
   the player with the highest mean after the next three rounds.
   Here are Meena's scores after two rounds.

	Round 1	Round 2
Meena	96	108

Meena needed a mean score of 105 to win.
How many points did she need in the final game?

⑥ Jack picks five number cards.

  a What is the mean of his five cards?

  b Jack picks a sixth card.
    The mean of the cards is unchanged.
    What number is on the sixth card?

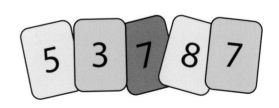

In the Census at Schools project, pupils were asked how many portions of fruit, vegetables, sweets and crisps they ate regularly each day.

The data for 30 pupils is shown in the table below.

Number of portions per day	Frequency			
	Fruit	Vegetables	Sweets	Crisps
0	3	2	9	4
1	8	7	4	15
2	9	8	5	4
3	6	10	8	4
4	2	0	2	0
5	0	1	1	1
6	1	1	1	1
7	0	0	0	0
8	1	0	0	0
9	0	1	0	0
10	0	0	0	1

Find the mean, mode, median and range for each of the four foods.

Points to remember

⊙ The **range** is the difference between the largest and smallest numbers in a set.

⊙ The mean, median and mode are different ways of finding the average of a set of numbers.

– The **mean** is the sum of the numbers divided by the number of numbers.

– The **median** is the middle number, or the mean of the middle two numbers, when you put all the numbers in order.

– The **mode** is the number that occurs most often.

⊙ For grouped data, the **modal class** is the group that occurs most often.

3 Using statistics

This lesson will help you to use simple statistics to compare two sets of information.

You can use averages and the range to compare two sets of data.

When you do this, it is important to explain your answer by giving reasons for your choice.

Example

William and Rosie are in different classes. The classes have the same regular spelling tests.

The mean and range for the spelling marks for the two classes are shown below:

Class	Mean	Range
William's class	8	6
Rosie's class	7.5	4

Which class is better at spelling?

You can say **either** that William's class is better at spelling because their mean was higher,

or that Rosie's class is better since their range is smaller, which means that they are more consistent at spelling correctly than William's class.

Exercise 3A

① Work with a partner. You will need the completed table on **S3.4 Resource sheet 1.1**. Look at the statistics for your survey on fruit, vegetables, sweets and crisps. Compare them with the statistics in the table below for 117 pupils from the Census at Schools project.

	Fruit	Vegetables	Sweets	Crisps
Mean	2.3	2.4	2.2	2.2
Mode	1	2	1	1
Median	2	2	2	1
Range	10	10	20	20

a Which set of data for fruit, for your class or for the 117 pupils, has the greater range?

b Which set of data for fruit has the greater mean?

c Write a sentence or two about the differences and similarities between the two sets of data for fruit. Say whether you think that your class eats more fruit than the 117 pupils.

② Repeat the comparison for vegetables, sweets and crisps.

① Here are the numbers of words in each sentence for two different newspapers:

Paper 1

21, 29, 17, 21, 8, 17, 17, 18, 11, 26,
12, 34, 12, 23, 14, 16, 20, 9, 12, 11,
21, 23, 8, 29, 14, 7, 15

Paper 2

10, 55, 24, 27, 11, 7, 35, 24, 11, 17,
39, 23, 17, 14, 22, 37, 24, 10, 28, 11,
18, 10, 13, 10, 18, 12, 33, 5, 6

a Calculate the mean number of words per sentence for each paper.

b Calculate the range for each paper.

c One paper is a 'broadsheet' (for serious readers). The other is a 'tabloid' (for a mass audience). Which is which? Explain your reasons.

② The manager of a basketball team needs to make a choice between two players. He has the number of points each has scored in their last ten games to help him.

Game	1	2	3	4	5	6	7	8	9	10
Player A	4	7	5	8	2	5	6	3	5	4
Player B	2	6	4	4	5	3	6	4	8	3

Calculate the mean and range.
Use them to help you to decide which player he should pick. Explain your reasons.

③ Amy has recorded the time it takes her to get to school for four weeks.
For two of those weeks she went on the bus. For the other two she walked.
The table shows the time she took each day.

Day	Mon	Tue	Wed	Thur	Fri	Mon	Tue	Wed	Thur	Fri
Bus	15	10	25	12	30	15	10	25	12	15
Walk	22	24	23	22	21	22	24	22	21	22

Amy hates to be late to school. Should she walk or take the bus?
Calculate the mode and the range. Use them to explain your answer.

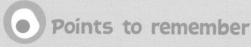

Points to remember

⊙ Use the range and a measure of average to compare two sets of data.

4 Representing data

This lesson will help you to draw graphs and charts, on paper or using ICT.

Exercise 4

You will need **either** the data you all collected in homework task 1 listing eight people's gender, age and the number of portions of fruit or vegetables they eat, **or** the sample data below.

Sample data set

Gender	Age	Portions eaten yesterday
Female	53	4
Male	40	5
Male	37	6
Female	33	1
Female	34	5
Male	54	4
Female	33	3
Female	45	6
Male	65	3
Female	26	0
Male	44	4
Female	28	2
Female	69	2
Female	37	8
Female	67	4

Gender	Age	Portions eaten yesterday
Male	27	6
Female	26	1
Male	55	6
Female	52	7
Female	84	3
Female	45	1
Male	49	16
Male	34	1
Female	17	4
Male	76	2
Female	29	0
Male	64	3
Male	48	1
Male	70	3
Male	24	0

Sample taken from www.stats4schools.gov.uk

Work in a group of four.

Choose one of the three questions below for your group to answer:

Questions

1. What proportion of people eat the recommended five portions a day?

2. Do older people eat more fruit and vegetables than younger people?

3. Do females eat more fruit and vegetables than males?

Before you analyse your data, think about these things:

- Do you need to draw a new table to reorganise the data?
  For example, you could group people by age or gender.

- Will you need to calculate averages and the range for the different groups of data?

- Would a graph or chart help to show patterns in your data?
  Will you choose a bar-line graph or a bar chart or a frequency diagram? Why?

- How will you share the work out between you in the group? Who will do what?

⦿ Points to remember

- ⦿ Choose charts and graphs that help to answer the question.
- ⦿ Make sure that you know why you chose that chart or graph.
- ⦿ Write down what each chart, diagram or calculation shows you about the data.
- ⦿ Check that you have answered the original question.

5 Interpreting and discussing data

This lesson will help you to:

- interpret statistics, graphs and chart, and say what they tell you.
- write and illustrate a short report of an investigation.

When you carry out a statistical project, you need to:

- ⦿ write it up so that others can understand what you did and what you found out;
- ⦿ use statistics to explain your findings;
- ⦿ illustrate your findings with graphs, charts and tables;
- ⦿ tell people how you came to your decisions.

Write at least one sentence to answer each of the questions below.

◎ **What was the original question that you investigated?**

◎ **How did you collect your data?**

  – Did you use a data collection sheet or questionnaire for your survey?

  – How many people did you ask?

  – Give an example of a question from your questionnaire and the answer boxes, or an example of some of the data that you collected on your data collection sheet.

◎ **How did you organise your data?**

  – Did you draw a new table, for example, to group ages, or to split the group into males and females?

◎ **What charts or graphs did you draw?** Put copies of them in your report.

  – Why did you choose those charts or graphs?

  – What did they show you about your data?

◎ **What statistics, if any, did you calculate?** Show your calculations and the results.

  – What did your statistics show about your data?

◎ **What conclusions did you draw?**

  – What do you think is the answer to your original question, and why?

  – How accurate do you think your results are?

◎ **How successful was your project?**

  – Did you experience any difficulties? How did you overcome them?

  – Would you do anything differently next time? Why?

⊙ Points to remember

◉ Choose charts and graphs that help to answer the question.

◉ Make sure that you know why you chose that chart or graph.

◉ Write down what each chart, diagram or calculation shows you about the data.

◉ Check that you have answered the original question.

How well are you doing?

Planning a project and collecting data

(1) *2002 level 5*

This advert was in a newspaper. It does not say how
the advertisers know that 93% of people drop litter every day.

Some pupils think the percentage of people who drop litter
every day is much lower than 93%. They decide to do a survey.

93% of us
drop litter
every day.

Gang
Up

ON LITTER

Do your bit. Use a bin.

a Jack says:

'We can ask 10 people if they drop litter every day.'

Give two different reasons why Jack's method might
not give very good data.

b Lisa says:

'We can go into town on Saturday morning.
We can stand outside a shop and record how many people
walk past and how many of those drop litter.'

Give two different reasons why Lisa's method might not give very good data.

Calculating and using statistics

(2) *2002 level 5*

Hannah went on a cycling holiday.
The table shows how far she cycled each day.

Monday	Tuesday	Wednesday	Thursday
32.3 km	38.7 km	43.5 km	45.1 km

Hannah says: 'On average, I cycled over 40 km a day'.
Show that Hannah is wrong.

a There are four people in Sita's family. Their shoe sizes are 4, 5, 7 and 10.
What is the median shoe size in Sita's family?

b There are three people in John's family. The range of their shoe sizes is 4.
Two people in the family wear shoe size 6.
John's shoe size is not 6 and it is not 10.
What is John's shoe size?

Completing the project

(4) The graph shows the spending habits of 45 pupils in each of Years 7 and 10.
Each pupil had to choose the one thing they spent most of their money on.

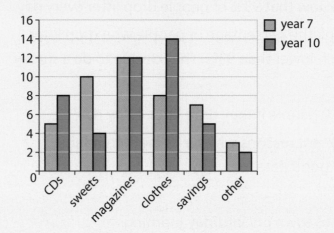

a Which year group chose clothes more often?

b What item was chosen by the same number of pupils in each group?

c Write two sentences about the spending habits of the two groups of pupils.

Constructions

This unit will help you to:

- identify parallel and perpendicular lines;
- estimate, measure and draw reflex angles;
- construct rectangles and triangles;
- identify some properties of 3D shapes;
- construct nets of 3D shapes.

1 Drawing line segments and parallel lines

This lesson will help you to measure and draw lines.

Did you know that...?

The ancient Egyptians were great engineers.

For example, the Great Pyramid at Giza was built around 2650 BC by King Khufu, who was also known as Cheops.

To build the Great Pyramid, the Egyptians must have known how to construct right angles and right-angled triangles.

Perpendicular lines meet or cross each other at right angles.

90°

Parallel lines are the same distance apart.

The perpendicular distance between them is always the same.

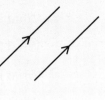

You will need a ruler, set square and sharp pencil.

1. Use a ruler to measure these line segments.

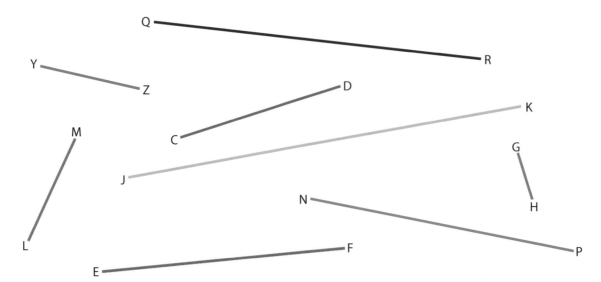

2. Use a ruler to draw these straight line segments.
   Label each line with its length in millimetres.

   a AB = 8 cm

   b CD = 40 mm

   c EF = 3.6 cm

   d GH = 72 mm

   e JK = 4.8 cm

   f MN = 53 mm

3. Here are a square, a cross and a rectangle.

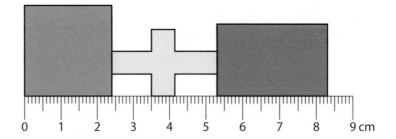

   Give each answer in millimetres.

   a What is the width of the square?

   b What is the width of the rectangle?

   c What is the total width of all three things together?

   d What is the total width of the cross and the rectangle?

   e What is the width of the cross?

4 A nonagon is a nine-sided polygon.
This nonagon is drawn on a grid of squares.

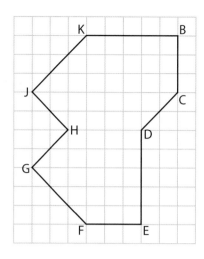

  a Which side is parallel to FG?

  b Which side is parallel to EF?

  c Which two sides are parallel to JK?

  d Which side is parallel to DE?

  e Which two sides are perpendicular to BK?

  f Which two sides are perpendicular to GH?

5 **a** Write down all the pairs of parallel lines.

  b How could you check that they
are parallel?

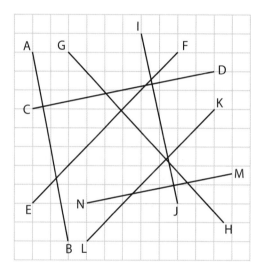

6 Use your ruler to draw a line segment 12 cm long. Label the line AB.
On line AB, mark a point C so that AC = 5 cm.
At C, use your set square to draw a line CD perpendicular to line AB.

> ## ● Points to remember
>
> ⊙ **Perpendicular lines** meet or cross each other at right angles.
> ⊙ **Parallel lines** are always the same distance apart; the perpendicular
>   distance between them is always the same.
> ⊙ Parallel lines do not need to be the same length.
> ⊙ Leave construction lines on your drawings.

2 Constructing shapes with right angles

This lesson will help you to use a ruler and protractor to construct shapes.

You can use a ruler and protractor or set square
to **construct perpendicular lines**.

- ◉ Draw a base line. Label it AB.
- ◉ Put the centre of the protractor at B.
- ◉ Reading from the outer scale, make a mark
  at 90°. Label this point C.
- ◉ Join BC.

BC is perpendicular to AB.

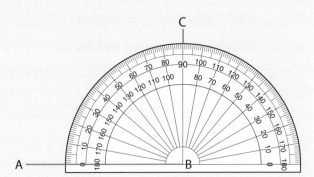

Exercise 2

You will need a ruler, protractor and sharp pencil.

1. Construct a rectangle with sides 5 cm and 7 cm.
    Measure the lengths of its diagonals.

2. Construct a square that has a perimeter of 28 cm.
    Measure the lengths of its diagonals.

3. Construct a rectangle that has a perimeter of 14 cm and an area of 12 cm².
    Measure the lengths of its diagonals.

4. Construct a rhombus WXYZ with diagonals WY = 6 cm and XZ = 8 cm.
    Measure the perimeter of the rhombus WXYZ.

5. Construct a square PQRS with each diagonal equal to 7 cm.
    Measure the length of one side.

6. Construct a triangle ABC so that AB = 2.5 cm, BC = 6 cm and angle B = 90°.
    Measure the length of side AC.

◉ Points to remember

- ◉ Draw a rough sketch to see what your construction will look like.
- ◉ Think where to draw the first line so that there will be room for the
  construction on the page.
- ◉ Leave construction lines on your drawing.

3 Acute, obtuse and reflex angles

This lesson will help you to use a ruler and protractor to draw angles and construct shapes.

A **reflex angle** lies between 180 degrees and 360 degrees.
To measure or draw a **reflex angle**, measure or draw the acute or obtuse angle and subtract it from 360°.

Example

Measure this angle.

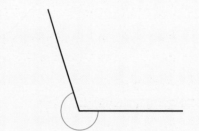

The reflex angle is just under 3 right angles (270°).
An estimate for its size is 260°.

Measure the obtuse angle first.
Take it away from 360°.
Reading the inner scale, the obtuse angle is 108°.
360° − 108° = 252°
The angle is 252°.

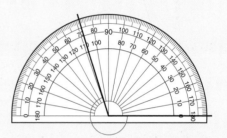

Exercise 3

You will need a ruler, protractor and sharp pencil.

1. Measure these acute or obtuse angles.

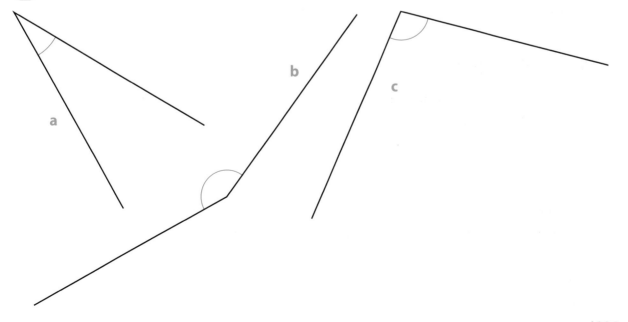

② Measure these reflex angles.

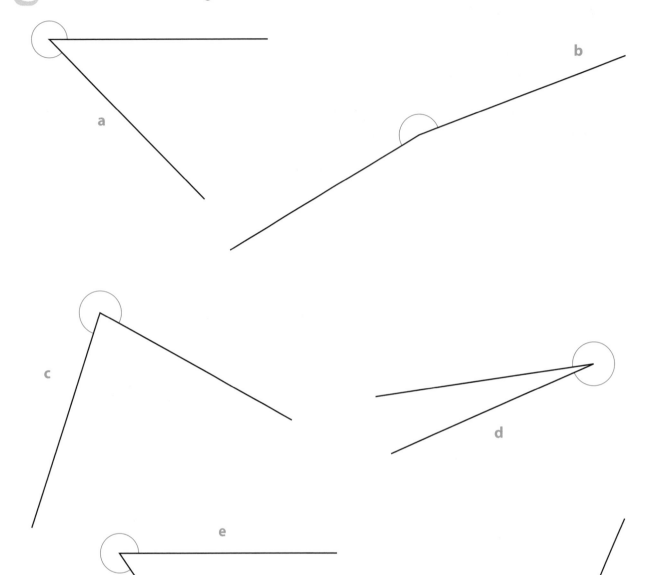

③ Use a ruler and protractor to draw and label these angles.

a   angle ABC = 47°   b   angle EFG = 123°

c   angle MJL = 220°   d   angle CDE = 318°

4 With a ruler, draw line segment AB, 5 cm long.
Now draw angle ABC so that it is 230°.

5 With a ruler, draw line segment AB, 5 cm long.
Now draw angle BAC so that it is 315°.

6 Each of the drawings below is a rough sketch.
Make an accurate drawing from each rough sketch.

a Rhombus ABCD

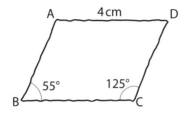

b Parallelogram WXYZ

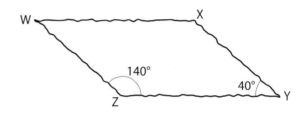

Extension problem

7 Make an accurate drawing of this isosceles trapezium.

Measure CD.

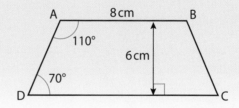

Points to remember

⊙ To draw a **reflex angle** with a 180° protractor:
 – subtract the angle from 360° and draw the acute or obtuse angle;
 – then mark the reflex angle.
⊙ Draw a rough sketch to see what your construction will look like.
⊙ Think where to draw the first line so that there will be room for the construction on the page.
⊙ Leave construction lines on your drawing.

4 Constructing triangles

This lesson will help you to use a ruler and protractor to construct shapes.

Example 1

Draw triangle XYZ with
XZ = 5 cm, XY = 6 cm
and angle ZXY = 30°.

First make a rough
sketch of the triangle.

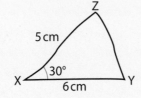

Draw a line segment XY
6 cm long.
Leave space above it
to construct the rest
of the triangle.

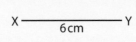

Draw an angle of 30°
at X.

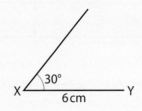

Measure from X a
distance of 5 cm and
mark it on the line.
Label this point Z.

Triangle XYZ is the
required triangle.

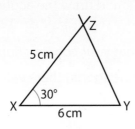

Example 2

Draw triangle ABC
with AB = 7 cm,
angle BAC = 30° and
angle ABC = 50°.

First make a rough
sketch of the triangle.

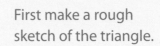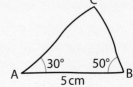

Draw a line segment
AB 5 cm long.
Leave space above it
for the rest of the
triangle.

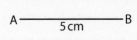

Use a protractor to
draw an angle of 30°
at A.

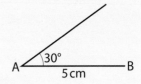

Use a protractor to
draw an angle of 50°
at B.
Label the point C.

Triangle ABC is the
required triangle.

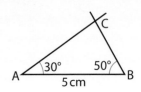

You need a ruler, protractor and sharp pencil.

1 Make an accurate drawing of these triangles, given two sides and the included angle (SAS).

    a 4 cm, 45°, 4 cm   b 3 cm, 90°, 4 cm

    c 5 cm, 30°, 7 cm   d 6 cm, 120°, 8 cm

2 Make an accurate drawing of these triangles, given two angles and the included side (ASA).

    a 45°, 6 cm, 45°   b 90°, 7 cm, 60°

    c 45°, 10 cm, 30°   d 100°, 4 cm, 30°

3 Sylvester is trying to draw a triangle with two angles and the included side of 120°, 5 cm, 70°.

Leroy says: 'You can't.'
Sylvester thinks he can.

Who is correct and why?

4 Among the triangles below, there are three pairs of congruent triangles.
Which pairs of triangles are they?
For each pair, write SAS or ASA as a reason.

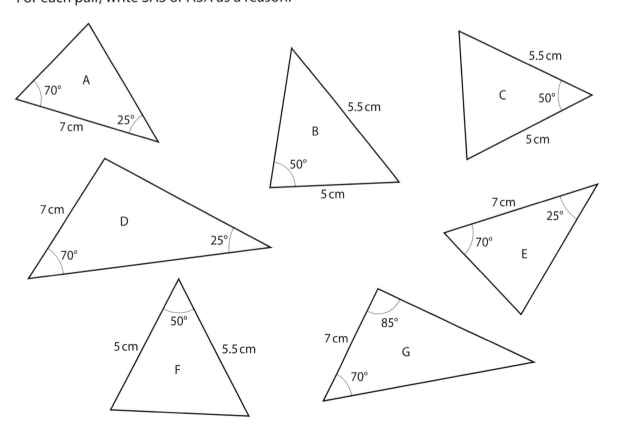

⊙ The sum of the two shorter sides of a triangle is always greater than the longest side.

⊙ **Congruent triangles** have the same angles and are the same size.

⊙ Two triangles are congruent if the have the same side-angle-side (SAS) measurements, or the same angle-side-angle (ASA) measurements.

⊙ **Similar triangles** have the same angles but are different sizes.

5 Nets of 3D shapes

This lesson will help you to construct nets of 3D shapes.

A **net** is a 2D pattern that when folded creates a 3D shape.
This cuboid measures 8 cm by 4 cm by 3 cm.

Its net could look like this:

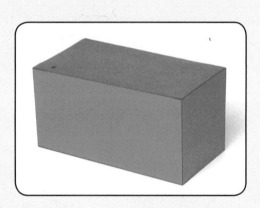

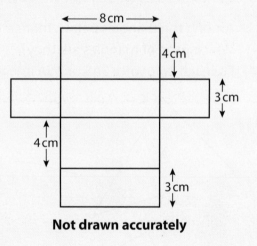

Not drawn accurately

Exercise 5

You will need a ruler, protractor and sharp pencil.

1. Make an accurate drawing of a net for a cuboid whose dimensions are
   length 7 cm, width 5 cm and height 3 cm.
   What is the total surface area of the cuboid?

2. Make an accurate drawing of a net for a cube of edge 4 cm.
   What is the total surface area of the cube?

3. A cuboid is 7.3 cm long, 4.5 cm wide and 6 cm high.
   Make an accurate drawing of a net for the cuboid.

4   Opposite faces of an ordinary 1 to 6 dice always add up to 7.

A dice has edges 3 cm long.
Draw an accurate net for the dice.

Write the numbers 1 to 6 on the faces in the correct place.

5   This triangular prism is 7 cm long.
Each of the end faces is an equilateral triangle with sides of 5 cm.

Make a sketch of a net for the triangular prism.

6   Margie is going to draw an accurate net of this prism.
The face at each end is a regular hexagon.

Before she starts she draws a rough sketch of the net.

Draw a sketch of the net.
Label each side of the net with its length.

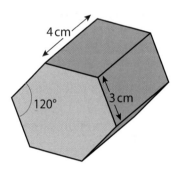

Extension problem

7   Here are three views of the same cube.

What colour is directly opposite the yellow face in the cube on the right?

Points to remember

⊙ A **net** is a 2D surface that can be folded into a 3D shape or solid.

6 Properties of 3D shapes

This lesson will help you to identify some properties of 3D shapes, including nets.

The photographs are of **three-dimensional shapes**.
'Three-dimensional' is often written as '3D'.

3D shapes have length, width and height.
They are not flat, like squares and circles.

A **prism** has the same **cross-section** all along its length
When you cut across it parallel to an end, you always get the same shape.

The base of a **pyramid** is a polygon.
Its other faces are triangles that meet at a common vertex.

Triangular prism

Square-based pyramid

Exercise 6

You will need a ruler, protractor and sharp pencil.

① Copy and complete this table.

3D shape	Number of faces	Number of edges	Number of vertices
Cube	6	12	8
Cuboid			
Triangular prism			
Pentagonal prism			
Hexagonal prism			
Triangle-based pyramid			
Square-based pyramid			

② Write down the shapes of the faces of:

   a a pentagonal prism

   b a square-based pyramid

   c a cuboid

   d a triangular prism

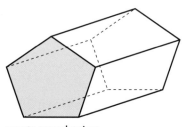

pentagonal prism

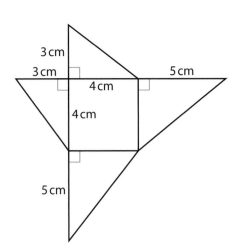

3 On the left is a sketch of a net of a pyramid. Use a ruler and protractor to make an accurate drawing of the net.

4 The picture shows a regular tetrahedron.

   a How many faces does it have?
   b How many edges does it have?
   c How many vertices does it have?
   d What shape are all the faces?
   e Each edge is 4 cm long.
     All angles of the faces are 60°.
     Make an accurate drawing of the net of the regular tetrahedron.

Extension problem

5 The diagram has six 1 cm squares joined edge to edge.
   a Explain why it is not the net of a centimetre cube.
   b Draw a different diagram with six 1 cm squares joined edge to edge that is not the net of a centimetre cube.

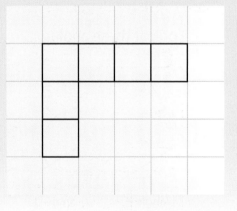

Points to remember

⊙ A **net** is a 2D surface that can be folded into a 3D shape or solid.
⊙ A **prism** is a 3D shape or solid that has the same cross-section throughout its length.
⊙ A **pyramid** is a 3D shape that has a polygon for its base. Its other faces are triangles that meet at a common vertex.

How well are you doing?

You will need a ruler, set square, protractor and sharp pencil.

Angles and constructions

1 *2006 Key Stage 2 level 4*

This shape is three quarters of a circle.
How many degrees is angle x?

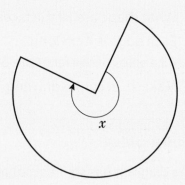

2 *2000 level 5*

Look at these angles.

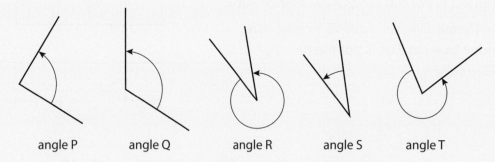

angle P	angle Q	angle R	angle S	angle T

a   One of the angles measures 120°. Write its letter.

b   Make a drawing to show an angle of 157°. Label the angle 157°.

3 *2006 Key Stage 2 level 5*

Here is a sketch of a triangle. It is not drawn to scale.
Draw the full-size triangle accurately.
Use a protractor (angle measurer) and a ruler.

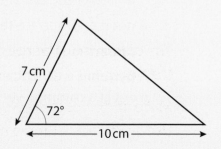

Nets of 3D shapes

4 *2000 Key Stage 2 level 4*

Which of these diagrams is a net for a square-based pyramid?

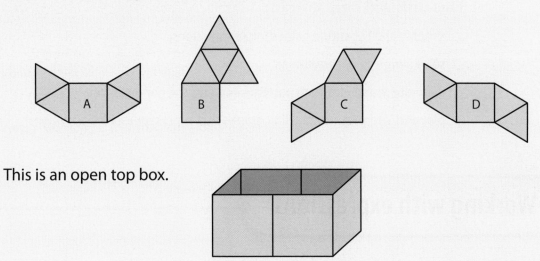

5 This is an open top box.

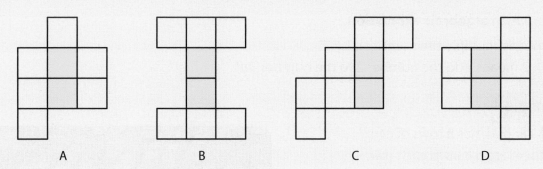

Which of these diagrams is a net for a similar box? The base is shaded.

A   B   C   D

6 Here is a triangular box.

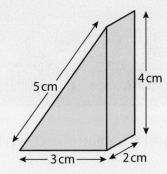

The diagram on the right is part of a sketch of
the net of the box. Two of its faces are missing.

Make an accurate drawing of the net of the box.
Use a protractor (angle measurer) and a ruler.

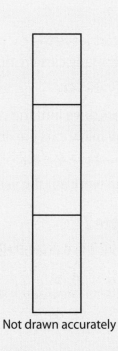

Not drawn accurately

A 3.4 Using algebra

This unit will help you to:

- simplify and substitute values into expressions;
- solve simple linear equations;
- generate sequences from patterns and find the general term;
- plot and interpret straight-line graphs that represent real-life situations.

1 Working with expressions

This lesson will help you to write, simplify and work out the value of algebraic expressions.

$3n + 2$ is an **algebraic expression.**

$3n$ means 'multiply the number n by 3'.

$3n + 2$ means 'add the number 2 to the number $3n$'.

Example 1

a   A car park has 8 rows of cars.
   There are n cars in each row.
   How many cars are there in the car park?
   $8 \times n = 8n$ cars

b   11 cars leave the car park.
   How many cars are now in the car park?
   $8n - 11$ cars

c   4 cars drive into the car park.
   How many cars are now in the car park?
   $8n - 11 + 4 = 8n - 7$ cars

You can work out the value of an expression if you know the value of each letter.

Example 2

Work out the value of the expression $8n - 7$ when $n = 10$.

When $n = 10$, $8n - 7 = 8 \times 10 - 7$
$\qquad\qquad\qquad\quad = 80 - 7$
$\qquad\qquad\qquad\quad = 73$

Like terms have the same combination of letters.
You can simplify an expression by collecting like terms.

Example 3

Simplify the expression $2p + 4q - 5p$.

Since $2p$ and $-5p$ are like terms they can be combined.

$2p - 5p = -3p$

So $2p - 5p + 4q = -3p + 4q$

$-3p$ and $+4q$ are not like terms so they cannot be combined.

Exercise 1

1 A binder costs k pence.
A pen costs m pence.
A pack of paper costs p pence.

Write an expression for each of these.

a   The total cost of 5 binders.

b   The total cost of 4 pens.

c   The total cost of one binder and
two packs of paper.

d   Your change in pence from £1
when you buy 4 pens.

e   The difference in price between a binder
and a pack of paper.

f   How much more 5 binders cost
than 4 pens.

g   Your change in pence from £10
when you buy 5 binders and 4 pens.

2 Work out the value of each expression when $p = 3$ and $q = 7$.

a $p + q$	b $q + p$	c $p + q - 3$
d $p - q$	e $q - p$	f $2p + q$
g $2p + 2q + 7$	h $2p - 3q + 2$	i $2pq + 1$

3 Simplify these expressions by collecting like terms.

    a $3a + 4a$

    b $b + 7b + 6b$

    c $2p + 3p + p$

    d $6w + 3w - 5w$

    e $2c + c + 5c + 8c$

    f $a - 6a + 3$

    g $14a + 3b - 5a + 2b - 4b$

    h $5a + 9b + a + 4a - 2b$

4 There are b large nails in each large box and c small nails in each packet.

    a Jason buys 3 large boxes and 2 small packets of nails. Write an expression for the total number of nails that he buys.

    b Jason uses 7 large and 5 small nails. Write an expression for the number of nails that he has left.

5 Copy and complete this table.

Expression	$n = 5$	$n = 1$	$n = 0$
$n + 2$	7		
$n - 4$		-3	
$5n$			
$2n - 3$	7		
$3n - 7$		-4	

Extension problem

6 Simplify these expressions by collecting like terms.

    a $2p + q + 3p + 4q$

    b $4x + 2y + x + 8y + x$

    c $2ab + 5ab + 2ab + 4ab$

    d $8x + 3z + 2x - 3z$

    e $8 + 2z + z + 6z + 2$

    f $2ax + 4bx + 5ax + 2bx$

Points to remember

- Each part of an algebraic expression is a **term** of the expression. For example, in the expression $3n + 5$ the terms are $3n$ and 5.

- **Like terms** have the same combination of letters. For example, $2b$ and $-5b$ and b are all like terms.

- You can simplify expressions by collecting like terms.

- You can evaluate expressions by substituting values for the letters.

2 Functions and equations

This lesson will help you to write equations from functions and functions from equations.

Did you know that...?

Diophantus lived in Egypt around the year 200. He wrote a famous book called *Arithmetica* which showed solutions of algebraic equations.

Some people call Diophantus the 'father of algebra'.

This is an **equation**: $y = 5x + 9$

You can write the equation as a **function** in x like this:

$x \rightarrow$ | multiply by 5 | $\rightarrow$ | add 9 | $\rightarrow y$

Exercise 2

1 I am thinking of a number x. What's my number?

a I add 6 and get 11. What is x?

b I subtract 9 and get 7. What is x?

c I multiply by 4 and get 36. What is x?

d I multiply by 3, add 15 and get 33. What is x?

e I add 4, then multiply by 7 and get 49. What is x?

f I divide by 7 and get 8. What is x?

g I divide by 5, add 4 and get 10. What is x?

h I multiply by 8, subtract 5 and get 27. What is x?

i I divide by 6, subtract 9 and get 1. What is x?

j I subtract 4, divide by 10 and get 6. What is x?

2 Write the equations as functions in x.

a $y = x + 8$ b $y = x - 7$ c $y = 3x + 15$

d $y = 9x - 23$ e $y = \frac{x}{4} + 6$ f $y = 16 + 2x$

g $y = 5x - 13$ h $y = 3(x + 7)$ i $y = 5(x - 14)$

(3) Write the functions as equations in x and y.

a $x \rightarrow \boxed{\text{add } 27} \rightarrow y$

b $x \rightarrow \boxed{\text{subtract } 19} \rightarrow y$

c $x \rightarrow \boxed{\text{multiply by } 11} \rightarrow y$

d $x \rightarrow \boxed{\text{divide by } 5} \rightarrow y$

e $x \rightarrow \boxed{\text{multiply by } 13} \rightarrow \boxed{\text{add } 8} \rightarrow y$

f $x \rightarrow \boxed{\text{multiply by } 9} \rightarrow \boxed{\text{subtract } 5} \rightarrow y$

g $x \rightarrow \boxed{\text{divide by } 3} \rightarrow \boxed{\text{add } 5} \rightarrow y$

h $x \rightarrow \boxed{\text{divide by } 2} \rightarrow \boxed{\text{subtract } 11} \rightarrow y$

(4) Write the inverse functions.

a $x \rightarrow \boxed{\text{add } 81} \rightarrow y$

b $x \rightarrow \boxed{\text{subtract } 76} \rightarrow y$

c $x \rightarrow \boxed{\text{multiply by } 29} \rightarrow y$

d $x \rightarrow \boxed{\text{divide by } 13} \rightarrow y$

e $x \rightarrow \boxed{\text{multiply by } 16} \rightarrow \boxed{\text{add } 32} \rightarrow y$

f $x \rightarrow \boxed{\text{multiply by } 25} \rightarrow \boxed{\text{subtract } 3} \rightarrow y$

g $x \rightarrow \boxed{\text{divide by } 9} \rightarrow \boxed{\text{add } 7} \rightarrow y$

h $x \rightarrow \boxed{\text{divide by } 6} \rightarrow \boxed{\text{subtract } 4} \rightarrow y$

Extension problems

Brackets change the order of operations.

For example, the equation $y = 5(x + 9)$ can be written as a function in x:

$x \rightarrow \boxed{\text{add } 9} \rightarrow \boxed{\text{multiply by } 5} \rightarrow y$

(5) Write the functions as equations in x and y.

a $x \rightarrow \boxed{\text{add } 15} \rightarrow \boxed{\text{multiply by } 7} \rightarrow y$

b $x \rightarrow \boxed{\text{subtract } 8} \rightarrow \boxed{\text{multiply by } 3} \rightarrow y$

(6) Write the inverse functions.

a $x \rightarrow \boxed{\text{add } 33} \rightarrow \boxed{\text{multiply by } 8} \rightarrow y$

b $x \rightarrow \boxed{\text{subtract } 17} \rightarrow \boxed{\text{multiply by } 35} \rightarrow y$

Points to remember

⊙ The equation $y = 5x - 4$ can be written as a function like this:

$x \rightarrow \boxed{\text{multiply by } 5} \rightarrow \boxed{\text{subtract } 4} \rightarrow y$

⊙ Given a value for x, work through the function to find the value of y.

⊙ Given a value for y, work through the inverse function to find the value of x.

⊙ The inverse of addition is subtraction.
The inverse of subtraction is addition.
The inverse of multiplication is division.
The inverse of division is multiplication.

3 Solving equations

Did you know that...?

The photograph shows mathematician Dr Tasha Inniss teaching her algebra class at Trinity College in Washington, USA in 2001.

Tasha Inness was one of the first black women in the USA to receive a doctor's degree in mathematics from the University of Maryland.

This lesson will help you to solve simple equations.

To solve an equation first work out the inverse function.

Example   Solve $x + 29 = 113$.

$$x + 29 = 113$$

$$x \rightarrow \boxed{+29} \rightarrow 113$$

subtract 29 $$\underline{x = 84}$$

$$84 \leftarrow \boxed{-29} \leftarrow 113$$

Exercise 3

1. Find the value of x.

   a $x + 16 = 23$ b $x - 34 = 47$ c $x + 10 = 6$

   d $x - 29 = 67$ e $105 + x = 123$ f $9x = 108$

   g $\frac{x}{3} = 7$ h $140 = 7x$ i $48 = \frac{x}{6}$

2. Find pairs of cards where x has the same value.

   $x - 7 = 24$ $6x = 42$ $x - 19 = 6$ $x \div 4 = 3$

   $x + 5 = 15$ $x \div 7 = 5$ $8x = 96$ $x + 6 = 37$

   $x + 8 = 15$ $3x = 75$ $x - 14 = 21$ $x - 7 = 3$

You can use any letters in the alphabet in an equation in the place of a number.
Normally lower-case letters are used, written in italics such as $a, b, c, d, \ldots$
Most often x, y and z are used, but you can use any letter.

3 Find the value of x.

a $2x + 9 = 19$ b $7x - 8 = 13$ c $54 + 6x = 66$

d $7x - 11 = 31$ e $5x - 17 = 18$ f $\dfrac{x}{2} - 4 = 5$

4 Find the value of each letter in these equations.

a $p + 9 = 51$ b $m - 17 = 44$ c $8t = 56$

d $a \div 11 = 8$ e $12 + s = 29$ f $w - 56 = 39$

g $v \div 21 = 5$ h $96 + z = 203$

Points to remember

- The left-hand side of an equation must always balance the right-hand side.
- Whatever you do to the left-hand side of an equation, you must do to the right-hand side.
- The inverse of addition is subtraction.
  The inverse of subtraction is addition.
  The inverse of multiplication is division.
  The inverse of division is multiplication.

4 Square and triangular numbers

This lesson will help you to recognise square and triangular numbers.

If you know the nth term, you can find any term by substituting its position into the nth term.

For example, if the formula for the nth term of a sequence is $3n + 1$:

the **1st** term is $3 \times \mathbf{1} + 1 = 4$

the **2nd** term is $3 \times \mathbf{2} + 1 = 7$

the **50th** term is $3 \times \mathbf{50} + 1 = 151$

the **100th** term is $3 \times \mathbf{100} + 1 = 301$

Exercise 4

1 Generate the first six terms of the sequences with these nth terms.

   a $5n$
   b $4n + 2$
   c $6n - 3$
   d $8n + 5$

   e $10n + 7$
   f $3n + 4$
   g $0.5n$
   h $3n + 0.5$

   i n^2
   j $\frac{1}{2}n^2 + 1$

2 Work out the 25th term of the sequences with these nth terms.

   a $10n$
   b $2n + 27$
   c $4n - 15$
   d $9n + 4$

3 Work out the 100th term of the sequences with these nth terms.

   a $3n - 7$
   b $3n + 19$
   c $n \div 5$
   d $0.5n + 1$

4 Look at this 8×8 chessboard and ask yourself how many squares you can see.

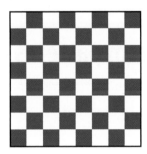

   a How many squares are there on:

     i a 1×1 board?
     ii a 2×2 board?
     iii a 3×3 board?
     iv a 4×4 board?

   b How many squares do you think there will be on a 5×5 board?
     Draw a diagram to test your conjecture.

   c How many squares are there on a 10×10 board?

   d How many squares are there on a $n \times n$ board?

5 For the pattern below, draw the next two shapes.
Write the number sequence that describes the pattern.
Explain how the number of squares increases and write the nth term.

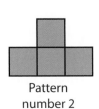
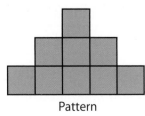

   Pattern number 1
   Pattern number 2
   Pattern number 3

A3.4 *Using algebra* | **239**

6 Work out the 100th term of the sequences with these *n*th terms.

a n^2 b $n(n-1)$ c $\frac{1}{2}n^2 + 1$

Points to remember

- The **nth term** of a sequence is the term in the *n*th position.
- If you know the *n*th term, you can generate the sequence by substituting $n = 1, n = 2, n = 3$, and so on.
- You can find any term by substituting its position into the *n*th term. For example, if the *n*th term is $3n + 6$, the 25th term is $3 \times 25 + 6 = 81$.
- The sequence of square numbers is $1, 4, 9, 16, 25, 36, \ldots, n^2, \ldots$
- The sequence of triangular numbers is $1, 3, 6, 10, 15, 21, \ldots, \frac{1}{2}n(n + 1), \ldots$

5 More sequences from patterns

This lesson will help you to find sequences from patterns.

Here is a **sequence of patterns** made up of pink and blue triangles.

   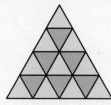

Pattern 1   Pattern 2   Pattern 3   Pattern 4

The next pattern in the sequence is made by adding another row of triangles.

The table shows how many triangles there are in each pattern.

Pattern number	1	2	3	4	5	6
Number of **pink** triangles	1	3	6	10	15	21
Number of **blue** triangles	0	1	3	6	10	15
Total number of triangles	1	4	9	16	25	36

The number of pink triangles is the sequence of triangular numbers.

The total number of triangles is the sequence of square numbers.

The formula for the *n*th term is $n \times n = n^2$.

1. Here is a sequence of patterns made up of hexagons.

  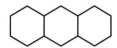 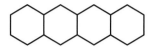

Pattern 1   Pattern 2   Pattern 3   Pattern 4

    a   How many hexagons are needed for pattern 5?

    b   Write the rule for the sequence.

    c   How many hexagons are needed for the nth pattern in the sequence?

2. Here are some patterns made out of tiles.

  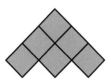

         Pattern 1   Pattern 2   Pattern 3

    a   Draw pattern 4 and pattern 5.

    b   Copy and complete this table.

Pattern number	1	2	3	4	5	6	7
Number of tiles	1	3	6				

    c   How many tiles are needed for pattern number 12?
        Explain how you worked out your answer.

3. Here is a sequence of patterns made up of crosses.

      Pattern 1   Pattern 2   Pattern 3   Pattern 4

    a   Write the rule for this sequence.

    b   Copy and complete this table.

Pattern number	1	2	3	4	5	6	7
Number of crosses	1	5	9				

    c   How many crosses are needed for pattern 20?
        Explain how you worked out your answer.

4 Jed lays paving tiles in a garden.
He uses red and grey tiles in this pattern.

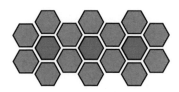

a How many grey tiles does he need if he uses just one red tile?

b Make a table to show how many grey tiles Jed needs for 1, 2, 3, and 4 red tiles.

c How many grey tiles does Jed need for 5 red tiles?
Draw the pattern to test your conjecture.

d How many grey tiles does Jed need for 10 red tiles?

e How many grey tiles does Jed need for n red tiles?

Extension problem

 5 Look at this pattern of straight lines.
The lines have been drawn to get the maximum number of crossing points.

0 crossings   1 crossing points   3 crossing points

a The next drawing will have four lines.
What is the maximum number of crossing points you can get with 4 lines?

b What is the maximum number of crossing points you can get with 5 lines?

c Write the numbers of crossing points as a sequence.

d Work out a formula for the nth term.

e Use your formula for the nth term to work out the number of crossings for twelve lines.

Points to remember

⊙ Sequences can be generated from patterns of shapes that follow a rule.

⊙ To help you to explain the rule for the sequence, look at the way the patterns increase or decrease.

⊙ Use the patterns to write a formula for the nth term.

⊙ To find the 50th term, substitute $n = 50$ into the formula for the nth term.

6 Interpreting real-life graphs 1

This lesson will help you to interpret straight-line graphs of real situations.

This graph shows the relationship between distance and time for a car journey.

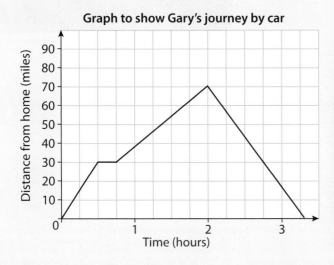

Graph to show Gary's journey by car

Exercise 6

1. The graph shows the flight of an aeroplane from London to Rome and back again.

   a At what time did the aeroplane arrive in Rome?

   b For how long did the aeroplane stay in Rome?

   c How many hours did the flight back take?

   d Work out the average speed, in kilometres per hour, of the aeroplane from London to Rome.

   e Estimate the distance of the aeroplane from Rome at 12:30.

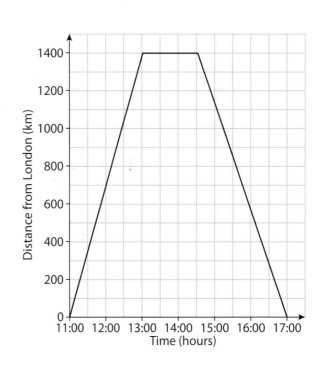

2 Carrie went for a country walk with her friends. She started and ended the walk at her home.

The graph below records Carrie's journey.

a How far did Carrie travel in the first hour?

b Carrie started the walk at 10 am. At what time did she first stop?

c How long was Carrie's first stop?

d At what time did Carrie arrive at her second stop?

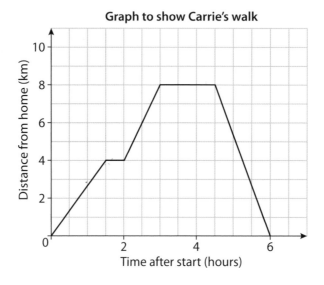

Graph to show Carrie's walk

Distance from home (km) / *Time after start (hours)*

e Carrie had a picnic with her friends at the second stop. How long did she take for the picnic?

f After the picnic they all walked home. How far did they walk from the picnic spot to home?

g How long did it take for Carrie and her friends to walk home?

h What was their average speed on the way home?

i At what time did they get home?

j Think of a journey that you have done or would like to do. Draw a distance-time graph for the journey.

Extension problems

3 Mike and Tammy are friends.

Each of them set off from home at 9:00 am.

Mike called on his friend Jodie.

They went on together to the park where they met Tammy.

This graph records the journeys of Mike and Tammy.

a How far is it from Mike's house to Jodie's house?

b How long did it take Mike to get to Jodie's house?

c At what time did Mike arrive at Jodie's house.

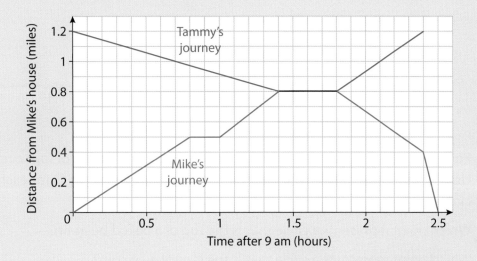

d How far is it from Mike's house to the park?

e How long did the friends stay in the park?

f How long did it take Mike to walk home?

g How far is it from Tammy's house to the park?

h How long did it take Tammy to walk home?

i At what time did Tammy arrive home?

j When Mike leaves Jodie's house he runs straight home. How long does it take him to run home?

4 This graph shows the circumference of a circle (C) against its diameter (d).

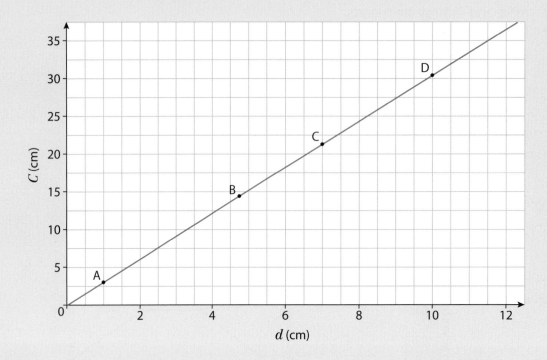

a Points A, B, C and D represent the diameter and circumference of four circles.
Use the graph to estimate the diameter (d) and circumference (C) for each of the circles.

b Which point represents a circle that is the top of a baked bean tin?

c Which point represents a circle that is the face of a 1p coin?

d Use the graph to estimate the circumference of a circle with diameter 9 cm.

e Use the graph to estimate the diameter of a circle with circumference 10 cm

f Estimate the circumference of a circle with diameter 20 cm.

g Estimate the diameter of a circle with circumference 50 cm.

h Karen is making labels for cylindrical tins.
One tin has a diameter of 7 cm.
What is the minimum width of the label for this tin?

Points to remember

⊙ A **linear graph** is one that consists of straight lines.

⊙ Read the labels and axes before reading any values from the graph.

⊙ Think about the context of the graph.

7 Interpreting real-life graphs 2

This lesson will help you to interpret straight-line graphs that represent real situations.

A graph can be used to change from one unit of measure to another.

You have met this type of graph before. It is called a **conversion graph**.

Here is a conversion graph which can be used to change miles to kilometres.

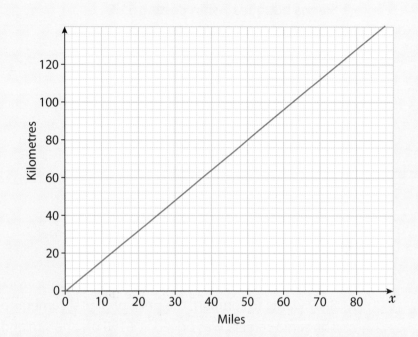

Exercise 7

1 This graph converts between gallons and litres.

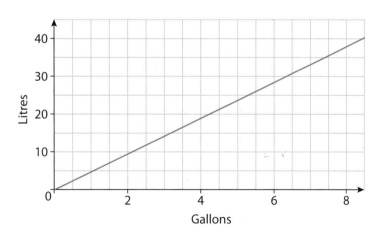

   a A café buys milk in 2 gallon containers. Estimate how many litres this is.

   b Hannah buys 20 litres of lemonade for a party. Estimate how many gallons she buys.

   c A hotel buys 4.5 gallons of olive oil. Estimate how many litres it buys.

   d Josh's car has a petrol tank that holds 35 litres of fuel.
      Estimate how many gallons it holds.

② This is a conversion graph from pounds (£) to US dollars ($).

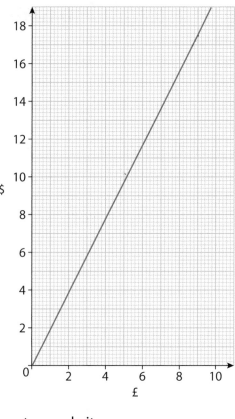

a Estimate how many dollars you get for £9.

b Estimate how many pounds you get for $10.

c Sienna bought a T-shirt costing $17. Estimate what it cost in pounds.

d Andy saw a pair of shoes costing £40. Estimate the cost in US dollars.

e Pat changes some money to take on holiday. Estimate how many dollars she gets for £100.

f Wayne is travelling from Dallas to London. He exchanges $150 for pounds sterling. Estimate how many pounds he will get.

g Dan orders some kit for his bike on the Internet. The price is given as $45. How much is this in pounds?

h Sally wants to compare the price of digital cameras on two websites. The same camera was priced at £150 on one site and $250 on another. Which is the best price?

③ The diagram shows a conversion graph between ounces and grams. Use the graph to change

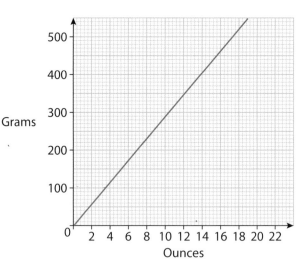

a 6 ounces to grams;

b 15 ounces to grams;

c 100 grams to ounces;

d 320 grams to ounces.

One kilogram is equal to 1000 grams.

ⓔ Use the graph to estimate the number of ounces in 2 kilograms.

Points to remember

⊙ A **conversion graph is used to change one unit of measure to another.**

⊙ Read the labels and axes before reading any values from the graph

8 Using ICT to draw graphs

This lesson will help you to interpret and sketch graphs.

 Did you know that...?

A graph shows patterns that are hard to spot just by looking a table of values.

A computer draws complicated mathematical patterns very quickly. This spiral is called a **Julia fractal**.

It was invented during World War I by the French mathematician **Gaston Julia**.

It was not seen like this until 1981, when the Polish mathematician **Benoit Mandelbrot**, who worked in the USA for IBM, first produced it using a computer.

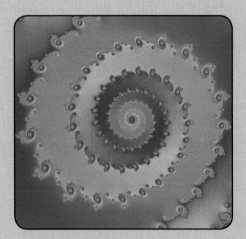

Exercise 8

Use a graph plotter on a computer or a graphics calculator.

1. Draw graphs of these equations.

   a $y = x$ 　　　　 b $y = x + 1$ 　　　　 c $y = x + 2$

   d $y = x + 3$ 　　　 e $y = x + 4$ 　　　 f $y = x - 1$

   g $y = x - 2$ 　　　 h $y = x - 3$ 　　　 i $y = x - 4$

2. Study the graphs you have drawn in question 1.
   Write what you notice about them.

3. Draw graphs of these equations.

   a $y = x$ 　　　　 b $y = 2x$ 　　　　 c $y = 3x$

   d $y = 4x$ 　　　　 e $y = 5x$ 　　　　 f $y = 6x$

   g $y = 0.5x$ 　　　 h $y = 0.25x$ 　　　 i $y = 2.5x$

4. Study the graphs you have drawn in question 3.
   Write what you notice about them.

Draw graphs of these equations.

a $y = -x$
b $y = -x + 1$
c $y = -x + 2$

d $y = -x + 3$
e $y = -x + 4$
f $y = -x - 1$

g $y = -x - 2$
h $y = -x - 3$
i $y = -x - 4$

 Study the graphs you have drawn in question 5.
Write what you notice about them.

Extension problem

7 **Sketch** these graphs on some blank axes.

a $y = x$
b $y = 2x + 1$
c $y = 5x + 2$
d $y = 7x + 3$

Now check your graphs by drawing them using the graph plotter or graphics calculator.

Points to remember

⊙ A relationship between two variables x and y can be shown in a
mapping diagram like this:

$x \rightarrow y$
$1 \rightarrow 3$
$2 \rightarrow 5$
$3 \rightarrow 7$
$4 \rightarrow 9$
$x \rightarrow 2x + 1$

⊙ This relationship can also be written as the **equation** $y = 2x + 1$.

⊙ The relationship can also be shown as a **linear graph.**

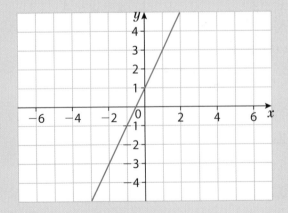

⊙ **A sketch** of a graph is a neat drawing not drawn to scale. Label any
important features.

How well are you doing?

- simplify and substitute values into expressions?
- solve simple linear equations?
- generate sequences from patterns and find the general term?
- interpret straight-line graphs that represent real-life situations?

Expressions and equations

1 *2007 level 5*

a Here is an expression.

$$2a + 3 + 2a$$

Which of these expressions shows it written as simply as possible?

A $7a$　　　B $7 + a$　　　C $2a + 5$　　　D $4a + 3$　　　E $4(a + 3)$

b Here is a different expression.

$$3b + 4 + 5b - 1$$

Write this expression as simply as possible.

2 *2007 level 5*

Look at this equation.

$$y = 2x + 10$$

a When $x = 4$, what is the value of y?

b When $x = -4$, what is the value of y?

c Which of the equations below gives the same value of y for both $x = 4$ and $x = -4$?

A $y = 2x$　　　B $y = 2 + x$　　　C $y = x^2$　　　D $y = \dfrac{x}{2}$

3 *2007 level 5*

Solve these equations.

a $32x + 53 = 501$　　　　　　b $375 = 37 + 26y$

Sequences, functions and graphs

(4) *2006 level 5*

Look at this sequence of patterns made with hexagons.

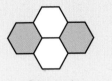  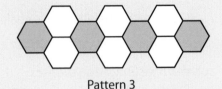

Pattern 1   Pattern 2   Pattern 3

To find the number of hexagons in pattern number n you can use these rules:

> Number of blue hexagons $= n + 1$
>
> Number of white hexagons $= 2n$

Altogether, what is the total number of hexagons in pattern number 20?

(5) *2007 level 5*

The graph shows the average heights of fir trees of different ages.

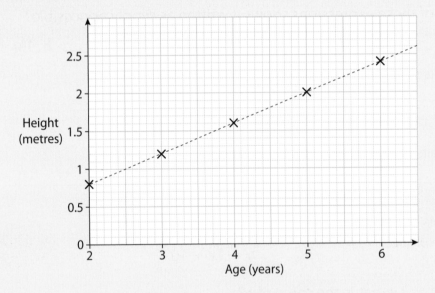

This table shows the cost of fir trees of different heights.

	120 cm to 159 cm	160 cm to 199 cm	200 cm to 239 cm
Cost	£ 20.00	£ 25.00	£ 30.00

a One of these fir trees is $5\frac{1}{2}$ years old.
How much is it likely to cost?

b One of these fir trees costs £ 25.00.
How old is the tree likely to be?
Copy and complete this sentence.

Between …… and …… years old

Probability 2

This unit will help you to:

- ◉ work out probabilities of equally likely outcomes;
- ◉ estimate probabilities using the results of an experiment;
- ◉ compare a probability that you have worked out with a probability based on experimental results.

1 Equally likely outcomes

This lesson will help you to work out probabilities of equally likely outcomes.

The probability scale goes from 0 (impossible) to 1 (certain).

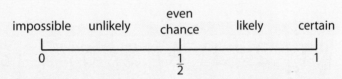

An event that has a 'fifty-fifty' or even chance of happening has probability 0.5, $\frac{1}{2}$ or 50%.

Probability values are written as fractions, decimals or percentages.

Example 1

A fair five-sided spinner is numbered 1 to 5.

Jane spins the spinner once.

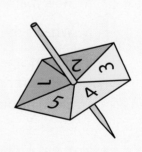

a Find the probability that the spinner will land on the number 4.

   The possible outcomes are 1, 2, 3, 4 and 5. There are **5** outcomes.
   The favourable outcome is the number 4, just **1** outcome.

   The probability that the spinner will land on 4 is

   $$\frac{\text{number of favourable outcomes}}{\text{total number of possible outcomes}} = \frac{1}{5} = 0.2.$$

b What is the probability of spinning an even number?

   2 and 4 are even numbers.
   The number of favourable outcomes is **2**.
   The total number of possible outcomes is **5**.

   So the probability that the spinner will land on an even number $\frac{2}{5}$ or 0.4.

Example 2

Six coloured counters are in a bag.

3 counters are red, 2 counters are green and 1 counter is blue.

One counter is chosen at random from the bag.
At random means that each counter is equally likely to be chosen.

Find the probability that the counter chosen will be green.

There are 6 possible equally likely outcomes.
The number of favourable outcomes 2, since there are 2 green counters.

The probability that the counter will be green is $\frac{2}{6} = \frac{1}{3}$.

Exercise 1

1   Robert has some digit cards labelled from 1 to 9.

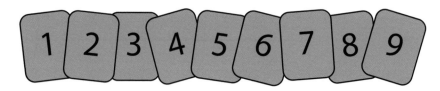

He picks one card at random.

a   How many different equally likely outcomes are there?

b   What is the probability of picking a 5?

c   Robert says: 'I am equally likely to pick an even number as an odd number.'
Is Robert right? Write **Yes** or **No**.
Explain your answer.

2   Faye has a different set of nine digit cards.

She picks one card at random.

a   What is the probability of her picking a 2?

b   What is the probability of picking a 4 or a 5?

3 Ben has 15 ties in a drawer.
7 ties are plain, 3 are striped,
and the rest are patterned.

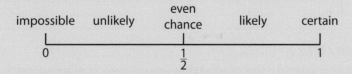

Ben chooses a tie at random from the drawer.
What is the probability that he chooses a tie that is:

a plain?   b striped?   c patterned?

4 Lucy picks a letter at random from the word **MISSISSIPPI**.
What is the probability that Lucy has chosen this letter?

a P   b M   c S

5 A fair six-sided dice is rolled. The table shows some possible events.
Copy and complete the table.

Event	Possible outcomes	Probability
more than 3	4, 5, 6	$\frac{3}{6} = \frac{1}{2}$
square		
prime		
odd		
multiple of 3		
less than 5		
even		

● Points to remember

⊙ **Probability is measured on a scale from 0 (impossible) to 1 (certain).**

impossible   unlikely   even chance   likely   certain

0    $\frac{1}{2}$ 1

⊙ **Probabilities are written as fractions, decimals or percentages.**

⊙ **An event** can have different **outcomes**.

⊙ If all outcomes have the same chance of happening, they are **equally likely**.

⊙ For equally likely outcomes, the **probability** of an event is:

$$\frac{\text{number of favourable outcomes}}{\text{total number of possible outcomes}}$$

2 Experimental probability

This lesson will help you to find probabilities from the results of an experiment.

You can estimate probabilities from the results of an experiment:

$$\text{experimental probability} = \frac{\text{number of successful trials}}{\text{total number of trials}}$$

Example

a Peter rolls a fair dice 30 times. Here are his results.

What is his experimental probability of rolling 6?

From the table, the experimental probability of rolling a 6 is 3 in 30, which is $\frac{3}{30}$ or $\frac{1}{10}$.

b How often should Peter expect to roll a 6?

He should expect to roll a 6 once in every 6 rolls. In 30 rolls, he should expect 6 to come up a total of $30 \div 6 = 5$ times.

Score	Frequency
1	7
2	5
3	7
4	5
5	3
6	3

Exercise 2

Work with a partner on Experiments 1, 2 and 3.
You will need a dice, a pack of playing cards and 0−9 digit cards.

Experiment 1

Draw a table like this one.

Score	Tally	Frequency
Odd		
Even		

Roll an ordinary dice 50 times.
Use your table to keep a tally of whether your score is even or odd.
It will be easier if one of you throws the dice and the other records the result.
When you have done this, work out the frequencies of the odd and even scores.

1 Use your results to help you answer the questions below.

a What was your experimental probability of getting an even number?

b What was your experimental probability of getting an odd number?

c What is the theoretical probability of getting an even number on a fair dice?

Experiment 2

Draw a table like this one.

Outcome	Tally	Frequency
Multiple of 3		
Not a multiple of 3		

Use a set of digit cards 0 to 9.

Put the cards face down. Shuffle them around, then pick one at random.

Use your table to keep a tally of whether or not you get a multiple of 3, that is, 0, 3, 6 or 9.
It will be easier if one of you has the cards and the other records the result.

Replace the card face down, shuffle the cards again and pick another card.
Record whether or not you get a multiple of 3.

Carry on until you have picked a card 30 times.
Now fill in the totals in the frequency column.

2. Use your results to help you answer the questions below.

   a What was your experimental probability of getting a multiple of 3?

   b What was your experimental probability of getting a number that is not a multiple of 3?

   c What is the theoretical probability of getting a multiple of 3 if you pick a card at random from a pack of cards 0 to 9?

Experiment 3

Look at a pack of 52 playing cards.

There are four suits:
two red suits, hearts and diamonds,
and two black suits, clubs and spades.

There are 13 cards in each suit.

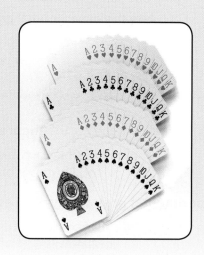

Draw a table like this one.

Suit	Tally	Frequency
hearts		
spades		
diamonds		
clubs		

Put the cards face down. Shuffle them around, then pick one at random.

Record which suit it is in your table.
It will be easier if one of you picks the cards and the other records the result.

Replace the card face down, shuffle the cards and pick another one. Record which suit you get.

Carry on until you have picked a card 20 times, then fill in the totals in the frequency column.

3 Use your results to help you answer the questions below.
   a What was your experimental probability of getting a heart?
   b What was your experimental probability of getting each of the other three suits?
   c What is the theoretical probability of getting a heart if you pick a card at random?
   d Compare your experimental results with the theoretical results.
      Do you think you did enough trials in your experiment?

Extension problem

4 Work in pairs to design your own experiment.
   You could use dice, a pack of cards or something else of your own choosing.

   Design a tally chart in which to record the results.

   Carry out your experiment.
   Calculate the experimental probabilities of the events in your experiment.

Points to remember

⊙ For equally likely outcomes, the **theoretical probability** of an event is:

$$\frac{\text{number of favourable outcomes for the event}}{\text{total number of possible outcomes}}$$

⊙ The **experimental probability** of an event is:

$$\frac{\text{number of successful trials}}{\text{total number of trials}}$$

3 Comparing probabilities

This lesson will help you to compare experimental and theoretical probabilities.

With a **fair** dice or spinner, all the outcomes are equally likely.
After lots of trials, you expect to get each outcome the same number of times.

With a **biased** dice or spinner, some outcomes are more likely than others.

You can work out the experimental probability of getting each outcome on a biased spinner or dice, but you can only work out theoretical probability if you know the bias.

Example

Paolo tosses a fair coin 40 times.
How many times should he expect to get a head?

The probability of getting a head is $\frac{1}{2}$.
Paolo should expect a head half of the tosses, which is 20 times.

Exercise 3

1 David has a bag of seven counters numbered 1 to 7.
Jade has a bag of twenty counters numbered 1 to 20.

Each chooses a counter from their own bag without looking.

For each statement, write **True** or **Not true** and explain your answer.

a David is more likely than Jade to choose a '5'.

b They are both equally likely to choose a number less than 3.

c David is more likely than Jade to choose an odd number.

d Jade is less likely than David to choose a '10'.

2 Mia threw a dice 180 times.

Here is her table of results.

a Work out the experimental probability for each outcome.

b Mia thinks that the dice is biased.
Is she right?
Explain your answer.

Outcome	Frequency
1	30
2	24
3	37
4	29
5	26
6	34

(3) Mia is given a second dice.
She throws the second dice 180 times.
Here is her table of results.

a Work out the experimental probability
for each outcome.

b Mia thinks that this dice is biased too.
Is she right? Explain your answer.

Outcome	Frequency
1	28
2	22
3	52
4	28
5	26
6	24

(4) A spinner has four sections labelled 1 to 4.

The table shows the results for 160 spins.
Do you think the spinner is fair?
Explain your answer.

Outcome	Frequency
1	42
2	39
3	35
4	44

(5) a Work with a partner to make a fair spinner.
Choose a shape on **S3.5 Resource sheet 3.1** if you wish.
Colour or number the sections so that each one is different.
Put a cocktail stick carefully through the middle
of the spinner so that you can spin it.

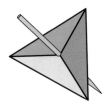

b What is the theoretical probability for each section of your spinner?
Spin the spinner 30 times and record your results in a tally chart.
Do you think your spinner is fair?
Explain your answer.

c Now make your spinner biased.
Stick a small piece of Plasticine or Blu-Tack to one section.
Spin the spinner 30 times and record your results in a tally chart.
What is the experimental probability for each of the sections of the spinner?

d Write a sentence to compare the experimental probabilities of your biased spinner
with the theoretical probabilities calculated beforehand for your fair spinner.

Points to remember

⊙ If a dice or spinner is **fair**, the outcomes are all equally likely.
⊙ If a dice or spinner is **biased**, some outcomes happen more often than others.
⊙ Experimental probability may not be the same as theoretical probability.

How well are you doing?

Probability

1 *2006 level 4*

This spinner has five equal sections.

Write five numbers that could go on the spinner to make the statements correct.

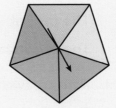

a It is certain that you will get a number less than 6.

b It is more likely that you will get an even number than an odd number.

c It is impossible that you will get a multiple of 3.

2 *2003 level 5*

a Jo has these 4 coins.

Jo is going to take one of these coins at random.
Each coin is equally likely to be the one she takes.
Show that the probability that it will be a 10p coin is $\frac{1}{2}$.

b Colin has 4 coins that total 33p.
He is going to take one of his coins at random.

What is the probability that it will be a 10p coin?
You must show your working.

3 *2001 level 5*

Mark and Kate each buy a family pack of crisps.
Each family pack contains ten bags of crisps.
The table shows how many bags of each flavour are in each family pack.

Flavour	Number of bags
plain	5
vinegar	2
chicken	2
cheese	1

a   Mark is going to take a bag of crisps at random from his family pack.

Copy and complete these two sentences.

The probability that the flavour will be .... is $\frac{1}{2}$.

The probability that the flavour will be cheese is ....

b   Kate ate two bags of plain crisps from her family pack of 10 bags.

Now she is going to take a bag at random from the bags that are left.

What is the probability that the flavour will be cheese?

c   A shop sells 12 bags of crisps in a large pack.

I am going to take a bag at random from the large pack.

The table below shows the probability of getting each flavour.

Use the probabilities to work out how many bags of each flavour are in this large pack.

Flavour	Probability
plain	$\frac{7}{12}$
vinegar	$\frac{1}{4}$
chicken	$\frac{1}{6}$
cheese	0

Solving number problems

This unit will help you to:

- solve problems with more than one step;
- work logically;
- find equivalent percentages, fractions and decimals;
- calculate with whole numbers, decimals, fractions and percentages;
- solve simple problems involving ratio and proportion.

1 Word problems

This lesson will help you to use number and calculations to solve word problems.

To estimate the result of a calculation:

- round numbers from 1 to 9, including decimals, to the nearest whole number;
- round numbers from 10 to 99, including decimals, to the nearest 10;
- round numbers from 100 to 999, including decimals, to the nearest 100.

Example 1   Estimate the answer to $472 \times 8.7 \div 58$

$472 \times 8.7 \div 58$ is approximately $500 \times 9 \div 60 = 450 \div 6 = 75$.

You can use the result of one calculation to work out the result of another.

Example 2   Calculate 237×3.1

First work out 237×31.
You can do this using the long multiplication method or the grid method.

Long multiplication method

```
     237
 ×    31
 ───────
    7110
     237
 ───────
    7347
```

Grid method

×	200	30	7	
30	6000	900	210	7110
1	200	30	7	237
				7347

237×3.1 is equivalent to $237 \times 31 \div 10 = 7347 \div 10 = 734.7$

Answer: $237 \times 3.1 = 734.7$

1 Estimate the answer to each calculation.

    a 54 × 36　　　　　**b** 215 ÷ 43　　　　　**c** 315.6 − 89.73

    d 345 × 85　　　　　**e** 18 ÷ 4.8　　　　　**f** 234.8 + 567.25

    g 578 × 123　　　　　**h** 399.2 ÷ 9.6

Find the answers to these calculations **without using a calculator**. Show your working.

2 Add 3.25, 97.8 and 4.654

3 Find the difference between 27.83 and 312.5

4 Multiply:　　　　**a** 428 × 67　　　　**b** 28.5 × 36

5 Divide:　　　　**a** 756 ÷ 28　　　　**b** 9.01 ÷ 17

6 A teacher needs 272 exercise books. The books are in packs of 16.
How many packs must the teacher order?

7 In one school year, Mimi goes to school for 39 weeks.
In each of the weeks, she goes to 35 lessons.
How many lessons is that altogether?

8 I buy a flat screen television costing £1576.
I pay £700 now, then I pay the rest of the money in 12 equal payments.
How much is each payment?

9 In a greengrocer's shop there are:

7 boxes of red peppers
5 boxes of green peppers
4 boxes of yellow peppers

There are 24 peppers in each box.
How many peppers are there altogether?

Extension problem

10 A football club wants to take 884 people in coaches to a match in London.
Each coach can carry 52 people and costs £420.
What is the total cost of the coaches?

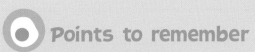

Points to remember

To solve word problems:

⊙ identify key information;

⊙ decide what operation is needed in each step;

⊙ change measurements to the same unit;

⊙ estimate the answer, then do the calculation;

⊙ check that the answer makes sense;

⊙ write the answer clearly.

2 Working with fractions

This lesson will help you to use equivalent fractions to solve problems.

To simplify a fraction, divide its numerator and the denominator by the same number. This is called 'cancelling'.

Example 1   Simplify $\frac{18}{30}$.

$\frac{18}{30} = \frac{18 \div 6}{30 \div 6} = \frac{3}{5}$

To change a fraction into an equivalent fraction, multiply the numerator and the denominator by the same number.

Example 2   Copy and complete $\frac{5}{8} = \frac{\square}{400}$.

$\frac{5}{8} = \frac{5 \times 50}{8 \times 50} = \frac{250}{400}$

To work out what fraction one number is of another, divide the first number by the second number and then cancel.

Example 3   What fraction of a whole circle is a 30° sector?

One full turn is 360°.

The sector of the circle contains an angle of 30°.

This sector is $\frac{30}{360} = \frac{1}{12}$ of the whole circle, cancelling by 30.

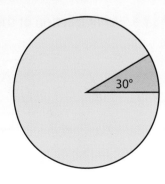

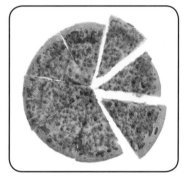  

1 Cancel each of these fractions to its simplest form.

a $\frac{7}{21}$ b $\frac{30}{50}$ c $\frac{48}{72}$

d $\frac{40}{56}$ e $\frac{100}{40}$ f $\frac{96}{6}$

2 Copy and complete these equivalent fractions.

a $\frac{2}{3} = \frac{\square}{24}$ b $\frac{5}{8} = \frac{\square}{56}$ c $\frac{2}{9} = \frac{14}{\square}$

d $\frac{9}{5} = \frac{27}{\square}$ e $\frac{13}{20} = \frac{\square}{100}$ f $\frac{12}{7} = \frac{144}{\square}$

3 What fraction is the blue shape of the red one?

a    b

c    d

e    f

4 What fraction of the circle is each of these sectors?

a 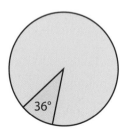   b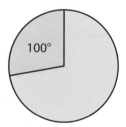

5 What fraction of the whole circle is a sector containing an angle of:

a 45° b 120° c 270°

d 80° e 225° f 200°

6 These fractions refer to sectors of circles. What angle does each sector contain?

a $\frac{1}{5}$ b $\frac{3}{8}$ c $\frac{7}{10}$

d $\frac{7}{9}$ e $\frac{13}{30}$ f $\frac{11}{18}$

7 Try this fraction investigation. Use only the digits **2**, **4** and **8** but as often as you like. Make fractions with a denominator less than 100.

Example: $\frac{2}{84}$

How many different fractions can you make that are equivalent to one half?

 Points to remember

⊙ To simplify a fraction, divide the numerator and the denominator by the same number.

⊙ To change a fraction into an equivalent fraction, multiply the numerator and the denominator by the same number.

⊙ To compare the size of fractions, change them to equivalent fractions with the same denominator.

⊙ To work out what fraction one number is of another, divide the first number by the second number and then cancel.

3 Fractions, decimals and percentages

This lesson will help you to find equivalent fractions, decimals and percentages.

Converting percentages to fractions or decimals

To change a percentage to a fraction or decimal, think of it in hundredths, i.e. divide it by 100. Simplify the fraction if you can.

Example 1 Write 7% as a decimal or fraction. 7% is equivalent to $\frac{7}{100}$ or 0.07.

Example 2 Write 25% as a fraction. 25% is equivalent to $\frac{25}{100}$ or $\frac{1}{4}$ (cancel by 25).

Converting fractions or decimals to percentages

To change a fraction or a decimal to a percentage, multiply it by 100.

To change a decimal to a percentage, multiply it by 100.

Example 3   Change 1.56 to a percentage.   1.56 is equivalent to $1.56 \times 100 = 156\%$

Example 4   Change $\frac{7}{20}$ to a percentage. $\frac{7}{20}$ is equivalent to $0.35 \times 100 = 35\%$

Converting between decimals and fractions

To change a decimal to a fraction, consider the tenths, hundredths and thousandths. Simplify the fraction if you can.

Example 5   Change 0.35 to a fraction. $0.35 = \frac{35}{100} = \frac{7}{20}$ (cancel by 5).

To change a fraction to a decimal, divide the numerator by the denominator. You can do this with a calculator.

Example 6   Write $\frac{3}{8}$ as a decimal.   Divide 3 by 8, so $3 \div 8 = 0.375$.

A dot over a digit in a decimal place indicates a **recurring decimal**.

0.8 is $\frac{8}{10}$, but $0.\dot{8}$, or nought point eight recurring, is 0.8888888…, or $\frac{8}{9}$.

0.16 is $\frac{16}{100}$, but $0.1\dot{6}$, or nought point one six recurring, is 0.1666666…, or $\frac{1}{6}$.

Exercise 3

1 Change each decimal to a fraction. Write each fraction in its simplest form.

   a 0.9   b 0.55   c 0.425

2 Change each decimal to a percentage.

   a 1.59   b 0.3   c 0.625

3 Change each percentage to a decimal.

   a 26%   b 148%   c 2.5%

4 Change each percentage to a fraction. Write each fraction in its simplest form.

   a 14%   b 195%   c 37.5%

(5) Change each fraction to a decimal.

   a $\frac{2}{5}$ b $\frac{13}{20}$ c $\frac{1}{8}$

(6) Change each fraction to a percentage.

   a $\frac{11}{25}$ b $2\frac{3}{10}$ c $\frac{17}{200}$

(7) Use only these digits:

    2   5   7   9

Use two different digits to make fractions less than 1.
For example, using the digits 2 and 5 you can make the fraction $\frac{2}{5}$

$$\frac{2}{5}$$

   a   How many different fractions less than 1 can you make?

   b   Write all the fractions you can make in ascending order.

(8) You will need **N3.6 Resource sheet 3.1** and some counters in two colours.
Play the game with a partner. When you play, look out for recurring decimals.

Extension problem

Use your calculator to investigate these problems.

(9) a   A fraction with its numerator and denominator each less than 20 is turned into a decimal using a calculator. The calculator display shows this.

            What was the fraction?

$$\boxed{0.4545454}$$

   b   What if the display shows this?

$$\boxed{0.5384615}$$

⊙ Points to remember

- ⊙ To change a fraction to a decimal, divide the numerator by the denominator, e.g. with a calculator.
- ⊙ To change a decimal to a fraction, consider the tenths, hundredths and thousandths.
- ⊙ To change a percentage to a fraction or decimal, think of it in hundredths, i.e. divide the value by 100. Simplify the fraction if you can.
- ⊙ To change a fraction or a decimal to a percentage, multiply it by 100.

4 Comparing proportions

This lesson will help you to work out and compare proportions.

A **proportion** means a fraction or percentage.

Percentages are more useful for **comparing the sizes of proportions**.
Remember to take account of the totals.

Example

Krishna gets 70% in a maths test.
Ravi gets 50 out of 70 in the same test.
Whose score is higher?

Krishna scores 70%.
Ravi scores 50 out of 70 which is
$\frac{50}{70}\% = 71.4\%$ to 1 d.p.
Ravi's score is higher.

Exercise 4

1. Which of these is more?

   a $\frac{3}{8}$ or 39% of 100 g   b $\frac{9}{20}$ or 42% of £100   c $\frac{4}{11}$ or 36% of 100 cm

2. Which of these is more?

   a 75% of 40 m, or 50% of 65 m   b 25% of 10 litres, or 20% of 12 litres

   c 40% of £15, or $\frac{1}{4}$ of £32   d $\frac{8}{13}$ of 39 kg, or $\frac{2}{3}$ of 33 kg

3. Two shops are selling this laptop at a discount.

   In Harry's, there is 30% off.   In Nixons, there is one third off.

USUAL PRICE
£450
30% off

USUAL PRICE
£450
$\frac{1}{3}$ off

   In which shop is the laptop cheaper in the sale?

4. At Bourne School, 53% of Year 7 are boys. In Year 8, there are 105 boys and 95 girls. Which year has a greater percentage of boys?

5. Janet took £50 of spending money on holiday. Rose took £48.

Janet spent £20 in the disco, £25 on presents and the rest on snacks.

Rose spent £18 in the disco, £24 on presents and the rest on snacks.

a Which girl spent a smaller percentage of their spending money on snacks?

b Which girl spent a smaller percentage of their spending money in the disco?

6. Robert asked 30 pupils which subject they liked best.

Subject	Number of boys	Number of girls
Mathematics	7	4
English	4	2
Science	3	3
Geography	5	1
Music	1	0
	total 20	total 10

a Which subject did 20% of boys choose?

b Which subject did 40% of girls choose?

c Robert said: 'In my survey, science was equally popular with boys and girls.' Explain why Robert was wrong.

d Which subject was equally popular with boys and girls?

7. Bag A holds 20 counters. $\frac{1}{4}$ of them are blue, $\frac{2}{5}$ are green and the rest are red.
Bag B holds 50 counters. $\frac{1}{10}$ of them are blue, $\frac{1}{2}$ are green and the rest are red.
Which bag holds more red counters?

8. In my first tin of paint, for every 2 litres of white paint, there are 4 litres of red paint and 4 litres of blue paint.
In my second tin of paint, for every 2 litres of white paint, there are 4 litres of red paint and 3 litres of blue paint.

Which tin has a higher proportion of red paint, the first tin or the second?

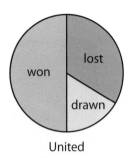

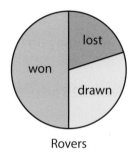

9 The pie charts show the results of football matches of two teams.

United   Rovers

United played 30 games. Rovers played 24 games.

a Estimate the number of games that United lost.

b Kathryn says: 'The two teams won the same number of games'.
Is she right? Write **Yes** or **No**. Explain how you know.

> ## Points to remember
>
> ⊙ A proportion is usually given as a fraction or percentage.
>   If 1 in every 4 beads is red, the proportion of red beads is $\frac{1}{4}$ or 25%.
> ⊙ You can compare proportions by using percentages.
> ⊙ Remember to consider the totals when you compare proportions.

5 Ratio and proportion problems

This lesson will help you to solve ratio and proportion problems.

Ratios are used to compare quantities.

For example, if there are 12 boys and 13 girls in a class, the
ratio of the number of boys to the number of girls is 12 : 13

The order of the numbers is important. The ratio 13 : 12 is
the ratio of the number of girls to the number of boys.

The **scale of a model or a map** is often written as a ratio.

This model aeroplane has been built to a scale of 1 : 80.
This means that 1 cm on the model represents 80 cm on
the real aeroplane.

Scale 1 : 80

① Rachel is threading beads in this pattern.

   a She has 8 more blue beads.
How many more yellow beads will she need?

   b She has only 6 more yellow beads left.
How many of her blue beads can she use?

② The instructions on a bottle of lemon squash say:

> *To make a lemon drink, mix one part of squash to five parts of water.*

James has made a jug of lemon drink.

   a Write down the ratio of squash to water in his jug.

   b James has used 200 ml of lemon squash. How much water has he used?

   c How much lemon drink does James have in his jug?

③ Ray is making mortar using three parts sand to one part cement.

   a Write down the ratio of sand to cement that Ray is using.

   b How much sand should Ray mix with 6 kg cement?

   c How much cement should Ray mix with 30 kg sand?

④ Ella and Daniel have won a prize of £40.
They decide to share it in the ratio of their ages.
Ella is 15 and Daniel is 10.
How much does each of them receive?

⑤ A cake recipe uses 150 g of sugar to 450 g of flour.
Sunil makes a cake using a total mass of 800 g of sugar and flour.
How much of this is sugar and how much is flour?

⑥ A model car has a length of 6 centimetres.
The real car has a length of 3 metres.

   a Write down the ratio of the length of the model car to the length of the real car.
Give your ratio in its simplest form.

   b The height of the real car is 2 metres.
What is the height of the model car?

These African sculptures are made from bronze.
Bronze is made from a mixture of tin and copper.

The two bonze figures have a ratio
of tin to copper of 2 : 9.

The bronze head has a ratio of
tin to copper of 3 : 13.

Which has the higher proportion of copper, the figures or the head?

 Points to remember

⊙ You can simplify ratios by dividing each side by the same number.

Example: 5 : 10 is equivalent to 1 : 2.

How well are you doing?

Number problems (no calculator)

(1) John chose a number.
He said: 'Dividing my number by 6 and then adding 8 gives the answer 13.'
What number did John choose?

(2) Work out the answer to $16.7 - 3.84$.

(3) In a café I buy two portions of rice and a curry. Altogether I pay £6.35.
A portion of rice costs 89p. What is the cost of the curry?

(4) *1997 level 5*

   a A shop sells plants at 95p each.
     Find the cost of 35 plants.
     Show your working.

   b The shop sells trees at £17 each.
     Mr Bailey has £250. He wants to buy as many trees as possible.
     How many trees can Mr Bailey buy?
     Show your working.

(5) Copy and complete these fractions.

   a $\frac{2}{12} = \frac{\square}{6}$ b $\frac{1}{2} = \frac{12}{\square}$ c $\frac{3}{\square} = \frac{6}{24}$

(6) Copy and complete these.

   a $\frac{3}{4}$ of $100 = \frac{1}{2}$ of $\square$ b $\frac{1}{3}$ of $60 = \frac{2}{3}$ of $\square$

   c $\frac{3}{8} + \frac{1}{3} = \square$ d $\frac{5}{6} - \square = \frac{1}{2}$

7 *2002 level 5*

Screenwash is used to clean car windows. To use it, you mix it with water.

Winter mixture
Mix 1 part Screenwash with 4 parts water

Summer mixture
Mix 1 part Screenwash with 9 parts water

a In winter, how much water should I mix with 150 ml of Screenwash?

b In summer, how much Screenwash should I mix with 450 ml of water?

c Is this statement correct?

> 25% of the winter mixture is Screenwash.

Write **Yes** or **No**. Explain your answer.

8 *2001 level 5*

Look at these shapes.

a What fraction of this shape is shaded?
Write your fraction as simply as possible.

b What percentage of this shape is shaded?

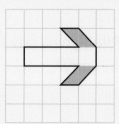

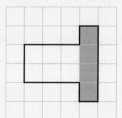

c Which shape has the greater percentage shaded?
Write **Shape A** or **Shape B**. Explain how you know.

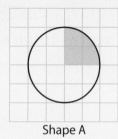

Shape A

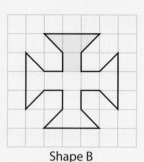

Shape B

Number problems (calculator allowed)

9 *2002 level 5*

Calculate:

a 8% of £26.50

b $12\frac{1}{2}$ % of £98

Functional skills 3

As little waste as possible

This group activity will help you to:

- identify how to tackle an unfamiliar problem;
- choose and use the mathematics needed to solve it;
- explain and justify your solution.

Background

A common problem faced by some industries is how to cut up lengths or areas of manufactured items.

For example, plastic tube is manufactured in fixed lengths.

When an order comes in, the fixed lengths of tube have to be cut up.

The aim is to have as little waste as possible.

Problem 1

Drain pipes

Plastic tubes for rainwater pipes are manufactured in lengths of 10 metres.

A customer orders these lengths for drain pipes.

    60 lengths of 3 metres

    49 lengths of 4 metres

    12 lengths of 7 metres

The manufacturer wants as little waste as possible.

What is the smallest number of 10 m tubes needed for the order?

The next problem is a related problem. Can you see the connections?

Parking on the ferry

A car ferry has six lanes for vehicles to park in.

Each lane is 60 metres long.

- Cars and caravans can park in any lane.
- Trucks and coaches can park in lanes 2, 3, 4 and 5 only.
- Lorries can park in the middle lanes 3 and 4 only.

These vehicles are waiting for the ferry.

30 cars each needing 4 m of space

10 cars with caravans each needing 9 m of space

3 coaches each needing 20 m of space

3 lorries each needing 30 m of space

Will they all fit on the ferry?

Be prepared to discuss your solutions with other groups.

Revision unit 1

This unit will help you to:

- revise the work you have done so far during the year;
- answer test questions.

Many of the questions are from National Curriculum test papers (SATs).

1 Whole number and decimal calculations

This lesson will remind you how to calculate with whole numbers and decimals.

When you have a calculation to work out, decide first how it should be done. Ask yourself:

- Can I do this calculation in my head?
- May I use a calculator or should I use a written method?

If you use a written method, set out your working neatly.

If you **use a calculator**, write down the calculation that you do.

Exercise 1

1. Decide which of these calculations should be done **mentally**, which should be done using a **written method** and which should be done with a **calculator**.

    a $91 + \square + 48 = 250$

    b Add 38.3, 152.56 and 1.675

    c What must you add to 5.4 to make 9.3?

    d $\square - 2547 = 2924$

    e Subtract 2250 from 8500

    f $7.65 - 6.85$

    g $1040.6 - 89.09$

    h $38 \times \square = 190$

    i Calculate 673×24

    j Calculate $899 \div 31$

    k Multiply 5.36 by 7

Do questions 2–5 **without using a calculator**.

(2) *2005 level 4*

    a Add together 3.7 and 6.5.   b Subtract 5.7 from 15.2.

    c Multiply 254 by 5.   d Divide 342 by 6.

(3) *2005 level 5*

Work out 374×23

(4) *2001 level 4*

The diagram shows how many miles there are between junctions on a motorway.

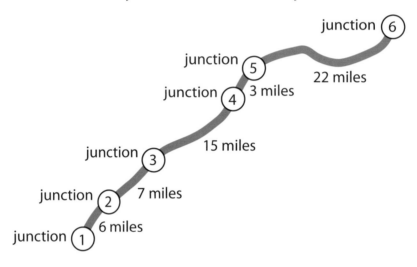

    a How many miles is it from junction 3 to junction 6?

    b Which junction is 31 miles from junction 1 ?

    c Mr Patel uses the motorway. He drives from junction 1 to junction 4 and back again from junction 4 to junction 1.
He does this every day for five days.
How many miles does he drive on the motorway altogether?

(5) *2003 level 5*

    a I pay £16.20 to travel to work each week.
I work for 45 weeks each year.
How much do I pay to travel to work each year?

    b I could buy one season ticket that would let me travel for all 45 weeks.
It would cost £630.
How much is that per week?

You may **use your calculator** to work out the answers to questions 6–8.
Remember to write down the calculations that you do.

6 *2003 level 4*

The table shows how much it costs to go to a cinema.

	Before 6 pm	After 6 pm
Adult	£3.20	£4.90
Child (14 or under)	£2.50	£3.50
Senior citizen (60 or over)	£2.95	£4.90

Mrs Jones (aged 35), her daughter (aged 12), her son (aged 10) and a friend (aged 65) want to go to the cinema.

They are not sure whether to go before 6 pm or after 6 pm.

How much will they save if they go before 6 pm?
Show your working.

7 *2005 level 4*

A restaurant meal costs the same for each person.
For 11 people the total cost is £253.
What is the total cost for 12 people?

8 *2005 level 5*

a $(48 + 57) \times (61 - 19) = \ldots$

b $\dfrac{48 + 57}{61 - 19} = \ldots$

2 Fractions, decimals and percentages

This lesson will remind you how to find equivalent percentages, fractions and decimals, and how to calculate percentages.

Percentage means 'per hundred', or 'in every hundred'.
For example, 47% means 47 out of every 100, or $\frac{47}{100}$ or 0.47.

If there is no quick way to find a percentage, find 1%, then multiply by the value of the percentage.

Example

Find 47% of £85.

1% of £85 is £85 ÷ 100, which is £0.85 or 85p.
47% of £85 is 1% × 47 = £0.85 × 47 = £39.95.

This is the same as finding $\frac{47}{100}$ of £85.

This is the key sequence if you are using a calculator to find 47% of £85.

$$4\ 7\ \div\ 1\ 0\ 0\ \times\ 8\ 5\ =$$

Exercise 2

Do questions 1−4 **without using a calculator.**

1. *2003 level 5*

   a Write what percentage of each diagram is shaded.

   i

   ii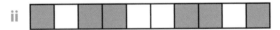

   iii

   b Explain how you know that $12\frac{1}{2}$% of the diagram below is shaded.

   c Copy the diagram below. Shade $37\frac{1}{2}$%.

   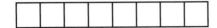

② *2005 level 5*

Copy and complete these sentences.

a   … out of 10 is the same as 70%.

b   10 out of 20 is the same as …%.

c   … out of … is the same as 5%.

Now complete sentence c using different numbers.

③ *1995 level 4*

On Friday, 260 people played different sports at a sports centre.

a   10% of the people played football.
    How many people played football?

b   40% of the people played badminton.
    How many people played badminton?

c   5% of the people played squash.
    How many people played squash?

④ *2003 level 5*

An adult weighs 80 kg. 60% of his total mass is water.
What is the mass of this water?

You may **use your calculator** to work out the answers to questions 5–7.
Remember to write down the calculation that you do.

⑤ *1999 level 4*

The cost in June for an adult for one week in a holiday camp is £85.
The cost for a child is 25% less.
What is the cost in June for a child for one week in the holiday camp?

⑥ *2004 level 5*

In 1976 the average yearly wage was £3275.
On average, people spent 17% of £3275 on their family holiday.
How much is 17% of £3275?

⑦ *1998 level 5*

The population of Greece is about 10 million.
37% of the population is aged 15 to 39.
About how many people is this?

3 Expressions and equations

This lesson will remind you how to simplify expressions and solve simple equations.

Letters can be used instead of numbers.

Example 1

There are three rows of chairs. Each row has n chairs.
Five more chairs are added. What is the total number of chairs?

The number of chairs in the three rows is $3 \times n = 3n$
Since five more chairs are added, the total number of chairs is $3n + 5$.
You could also write this as $5 + 3n$ chairs.

The value of an expression can be worked out if the value of each letter is known.

Example 2

Work out the value of the expression $3n + 5$ when $n = 10$.

$3n + 5 = 3 \times n + 5$
When $n = 10$, $3n + 5 = 3 \times 10 + 5 = 30 + 5 = 35$

An expression can be simplified by collecting like terms.

Example 3

Simplify $3x + 2y - 3y + 5x$.

Collect like terms together to write:
$3x + 2y - 3y + 5x = 3x + 5x + 2y - 3y$
$3x + 5x = 8x$ and $2y - 3y = -1y = -y$
so $3x + 2y - 3y + 5x = 8x - y$

The left-hand side of an equation must balance with the right-hand side of the equation. To keep the balance, do the same to the left-hand side and the right-hand side of the equation.

Example 4

Solve $3x + 5 = 17$.

Subtract 5 from both sides: $\quad 3x + 5 - 5 = 17 - 5$

$$3x = 12$$

Divide both sides by 3: $\qquad 3x \div 3 = 12 \div 3$

$$x = 4$$

Exercise 3

(1) *2001 level 5*

A teacher has 5 full packets of mints and 6 single mints.
The number of mints inside each packet is the same.

The teacher tells the class:

'Write an expression to show how many mints there are altogether.
Call the number of mints inside each packet y.'

Here are some of the expressions that the pupils write:

$$5 + 6 + y \qquad 5y6 \qquad 5y + 6$$

$$6 + 5y \qquad 5 + 6y \qquad (5 + 6) \times y$$

a Write down two expressions that are correct.

b A pupil says: 'I think the teacher has a total of 56 mints.'
Could the pupil be correct? Write **Yes** or **No**.
Explain how you know.

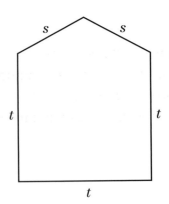

2 *1995 level 4*

The perimeter of this shape is $3t + 2s$.

$$p = 3t + 2s$$

Write an expression for the perimeter of each of the shapes below.

Write each expression in its simplest form.

a

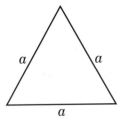

b

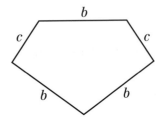

c

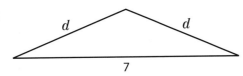

d

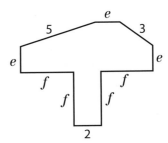

3 *2003 level 5*

Simplify these expressions.

a $5k + 7 + 3k$

b $k + 1 + k + 4$

4 *2002 level 5*

a When $x = 5$, work out the values of these expressions.

$2x + 13$ $5x - 5$ $3 + 6x$

b When $2y + 11 = 17$, work out the value of y.
Show your working.

5 *2005 level 5*

Solve these equations.

a $3y + 1 = 16$ **b** $18 = 4k + 6$

c $2k + 3 = 11$ **d** $2t + 3 = -11$

2004 level 5

Here is a magic square.
The letters represent numbers.
The sum of the numbers in each row,
column and diagonal is the same.

$a + b$	$a - b + c$	$a - c$
$a - b - c$	a	$a + b + c$
$a + c$	$a + b - c$	$a - b$

a Copy and complete this magic square.

Use the values $a = 10, b = 3, c = 5$.

		5
	10	
15		

b I used different values for a, b and c to complete the magic square.

What values for a, b and c did I use?

20	21	7
3	16	29
25	11	12

◉ Points to remember

- $3n + 5$ is an algebraic **expression**. An expression has at least one letter.
- Each part of an expression is a **term** of the expression.
  For example, the terms of the expression $3n + 5$ are $3n$ and 5.
- **Like terms** have the same combination of letters.
  For example, $2x$ and $5x$ and x are all like terms.
- You can simplify an expression by collecting like terms.
- The equation $x + y = 9$ has an infinite number of solutions.
- The equation $x + 3 = 10$ has only one solution, which is $x = 7$.
- The left-hand side of an equation must always balance the right-hand side.

4 Charts, graphs and simple statistics

This lesson will remind you how to interpret graphs and charts, and find the mode, median, mean and range of a small set of data.

When you answer questions about graphs and charts, look at:

- the **title** so you know what the graph or chart is about;
- the **labels and scales** on the axes so you can interpret the values;
- the **key**, if there is one.

The **mode, median and mean** are different ways of finding the average of a set of numbers.

- The **mode** is the number that occurs most often.
- The **mean** is found by adding up all the numbers and dividing by the number of numbers.
- The **median** is the middle number, or the mean of the middle two numbers, when all the numbers are arranged in order.
- The **range** shows the spread of the numbers. It is the difference between the highest number in the set and the lowest number.

Example

Tony plays cricket.
The numbers of runs Tony scores in each of 10 innings are:

20   35   17   1   14   15   5   13   2   6

a Work out Tony's mean score.

Tony's mean score is:

$$\frac{20 + 35 + 17 + 1 + 14 + 15 + 5 + 13 + 2 + 6}{10} = \frac{128}{10} = 12.8$$

b Work out Tony's median score.

Tony's scores arranged in order are:

1   2   5   6   13   14   15   17   20   35

The middle two numbers are 13 and 14, and their mean is $\frac{13 + 14}{2} = 13.5$.

So Tony's median score is 13.5.

c Work out the range in Tony's score.

Tony's minimum score is 1. His maximum score is 35. The range is $35 - 1 = 34$.

Exercise 4

(1) *1998 KS2 level 5*

Here is a bar chart showing rainfall.

Kim draws a dotted line on the bar chart.

She says: 'The dotted line on the chart shows the mean rainfall for the four months.'

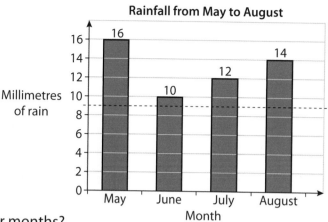

a Use the chart to explain why Kim cannot be correct.

b What is the mean rainfall for the four months?

(2) *1997 KS2 level 5*

a Write down three different numbers so that the mean of the three numbers is 9.

b Write down five numbers so that the mode of the five numbers is 11.

(3) *2004 level 4*

The bar charts show how many pupils went to a maths club.

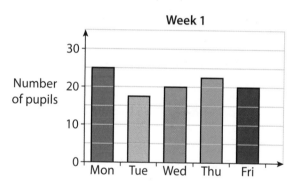

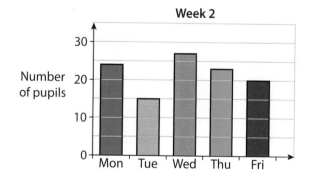

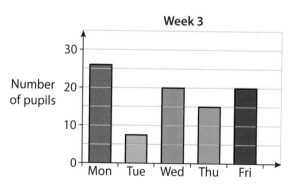

Is each statement below true or false, or is there not enough information to tell? Explain your answer each time.

a In each of these weeks, the day with the most pupils was Monday.

b In each of these weeks, the same number of pupils went to the club on Friday.

c In each of these weeks, the same pupils went to the club on Friday.

The diagram shows what pupils in Years 7, 8 and 9 choose to do at lunch time.

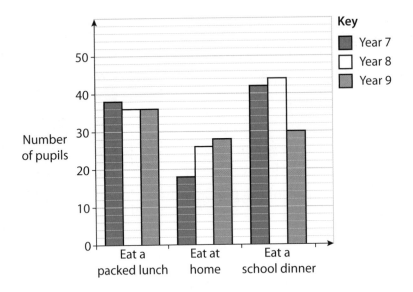

a   A pupil from each year group is chosen at random. For each year, write down if they are most likely to eat a packed lunch, or eat at home, or eat a school dinner.

b   How many more pupils are there in Year 8 than Year 9? Show your working.

(5) *2006 KS2 level 5*

This chart shows the number of books some children read last month.

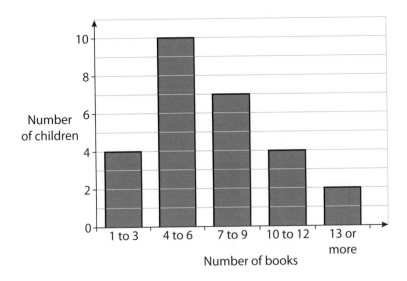

a   How many children altogether read more than 9 books?

b   7 children read 4 books. 1 child read 5 books.
Lin says, 'That means 2 children read 6 books'.
Explain how she can work this out from the chart.

Year 8 Optional Test level 5

The pie charts show how pupils answered three questions about teachers.

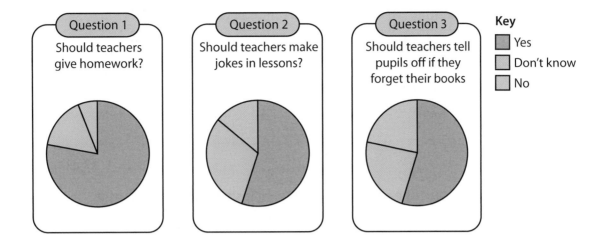

a What was the least common answer to question 2?

b What was the modal answer to question 3?

c About what proportion of pupils answered 'yes' to question 1?

7 *2000 level 4*

A pupil recorded how much rain fell on 5 different days. Here are her results.

	Amount in cm
Monday	0.2
Tuesday	0.8
Wednesday	0.5
Thursday	0.25
Friday	0.05

a On which day did the most rain fall?

b On which day did the least rain fall?

c How much more rain fell on Wednesday than on Thursday?

d How much rain fell altogether on Monday, Tuesday and Wednesday? Write your answer in centimetres.

e Now write your answer to part **d** in millimetres.

8 *2002 level 5*

Hannah went on a cycling holiday. The table shows how far she cycled each day.

Monday	Tuesday	Wednesday	Thursday
32.3 km	38.7 km	43.5 km	45.1 km

Hannah says: 'On average, I cycled over 40 km a day'.
Show that Hannah is wrong.

9 *1995 level 5*

Lisa works in a shoe shop.
She recorded the size of each pair of trainers that she sold during a week.
This is what she wrote down.

	Sizes of trainers sold						
Monday	7	7	5	6			
Tuesday	6	4	4	8			
Wednesday	5	8	6	7	5		
Thursday	7	4	5				
Friday	7	4	9	5	7	8	
Saturday	6	5	7	6	9	4	7

a Use a tallying method to make a table showing how many pairs of trainers of each size were sold during the whole week.

b Which size of trainer did Lisa sell the most of?

c Lisa said: 'Most of the trainers sold were bigger than size 6'.
How can you tell from your table that Lisa was wrong?

⦿ **Points to remember**

⊙ The **mode**, **median** and **mean** are different ways of finding the average of a set of numbers.

⊙ The **range** shows the spread of the numbers.

⊙ Graphs and charts are useful for showing features and making comparisons.

⊙ When you answer questions about graphs and charts, look at the title, the labels and scales on the axes, and any key.

⊙ When you compare two graphs, look for similarities and differences.

5 Probability

This lesson will remind you how to work out probabilities.

Probability scale

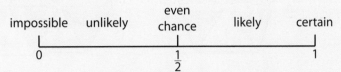

Remember to write probabilities as fractions, decimals or percentages.

If the outcomes are equally likely, the **theoretical probability** of an event is:

$$\frac{\text{number of favourable outcomes}}{\text{total number of possible outcomes}}$$

The **experimental probability** of an event is:

$$\frac{\text{number of successful trials}}{\text{total number of trials}}$$

When you repeat an experiment you can get different results each time.

Example 1

On the probability scale, mark with an arrow the probability that it will rain in Manchester during April.

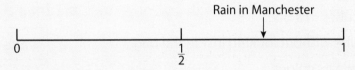

As it is likely that it will rain in Manchester during April, the probability is between $\frac{1}{2}$ and 1. So the arrow can be anywhere between $\frac{1}{2}$ and 1.

Example 2

A fair five-sided spinner is numbered 1 to 5.
Jonathan spins the spinner once.
Find the probability that the spinner will land on an even number.

The possible outcomes are 1, 2, 3, 4 and 5. There are 5 possible outcomes.
2 and 4 are even numbers. The number of favourable outcomes is 2.
The probability that the spinner will land on 2 or 4 is:

$$\frac{\text{number of favourable outcomes}}{\text{total number of possible outcomes}} = \frac{2}{5} = 0.4$$

1 *2000 level 4*

a The diagram shows spinner A and spinner B.

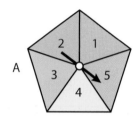 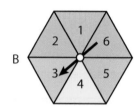

Which spinner gives you the best chance to get 1?
Explain why you chose that answer.

b Here are two different spinners.
The spinners are the same shape but different sizes.

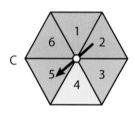 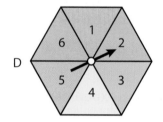

Which spinner gives you the best chance to get 3? Explain why you chose that answer.

2 *1996 level 4*

There are 30 cubes in a bag.

Kim takes a cube without looking inside the bag.

She writes down its colour.

She then puts the cube back in the bag.

She does this 30 times.

red	7
white	3
black	11
green	4
yellow	5

Kim records her results in a table.

a Kim says: 'There must be 7 red cubes in the bag, because there are 7 reds in my chart.' Explain why Kim is wrong.

b What is the smallest number of green cubes there could be in the bag?

c Kim says: 'There cannot be any blue cubes in the bag, because there are no blues in my chart.' Explain why Kim is wrong.

d Kim takes one more cube out of the bag. What colour is the cube most likely to be? Use the results in the table to help you to decide.

3 *2000 level 4*

A class has some gold tokens and some silver tokens.
The tokens are all the same size.
The teacher puts 4 gold tokens and 1 silver token in a bag.

a Leah is going to take one token out of the bag without looking. She says:

> There are two colours, so it is just as likely
> that I will get a gold token as a silver token.

Explain why Leah is wrong.

b How many more silver tokens should the teacher put in the bag to make it just as likely that Leah will get a gold token as a silver token?

c Jack has a different bag with 8 tokens in it.
It is more likely that Jack will take a gold token than a silver token from his bag.
How many gold tokens might there be in Jack's bag?

4 *1999 level 4*

Bryn has some bags with some black beads and some white beads.
He is going to take a bead from each bag without looking.

Match the pictures to the statements.

    A   B   C   D   E

a It is impossible that Bryn will take a black bead from this bag.

b It is unlikely that Bryn will take a black bead from this bag.

c It is equally likely that Bryn will take a black bead or a white bead from this bag.

d It is likely that Bryn will take a black bead from this bag.

e It is certain that Bryn will take a black bead from this bag.

Here are four spinners, labelled P, Q, R and S.

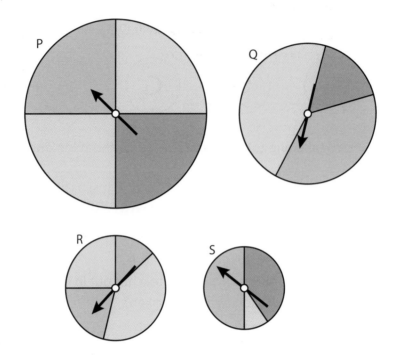

a Which spinner gives the greatest chance that the arrow will land on blue?

b Which spinner gives the smallest chance that the arrow will land on purple?

c Draw a copy of this spinner.
  Shade it so that it is certain that the arrow will land on the shaded part.

d Draw another copy of the spinner.
  This time shade it so that there is a 50% chance that the arrow will land on the shaded part.

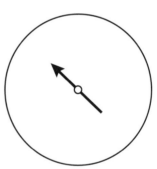

⑥ *2007 level 5*

Fred has a bag of sweets.
He is going to take a sweet from the bag at random.

a What is the probability that Fred will get a black sweet?

b Copy and complete this sentence.
  Fill in the missing colour.

  The probability that Fred will get a … sweet is $\frac{1}{4}$.

Contents
3 yellow sweets
5 green sweets
7 red sweets
4 purple sweets
1 black sweet

7 *2006 level 5*

I buy 12 packets of cat food in a box.
The table shows the different varieties.

a I am going to take a packet at random from the box.
What is the probability that it will be cod?

b My cat eats all the packets of cod.
I am going to take a packet at random
from the ones left in the box.
What is the probability that it will be salmon?

Variety	Number of packets
cod	3
salmon	3
trout	3
tuna	3

8 *2007 level 5*

The diagram shows five fair spinners with blue and white sectors.
Each spinner is divided into equal sectors.

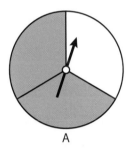
A

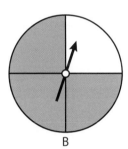
B

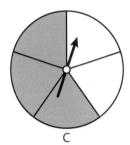
C

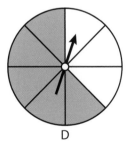
D

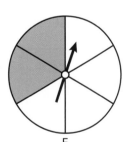
E

I am going to spin all the pointers.

a For one of the spinners, the probability of spinning blue is $\frac{3}{4}$.

Which spinner is this? Write its letter.

b For two of the spinners, the probability of spinning blue is
more than 60% but less than 70%.

Which two spinners are these? Write their letters.

a Joe has these cards:

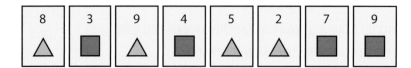

Sara takes a card without looking.

Joe says: 'On Sara's card, ■ is more likely than △.'

Explain why Joe is wrong.

b Here are some words and phrases: **impossible   not likely   certain   likely**

Choose a word or a phrase to copy and complete the sentences below.

It is ……………… that the number on Sara's card will be smaller than 10.

It is ……………… that the number on Sara's card will be an odd number.

c Joe still has these cards:

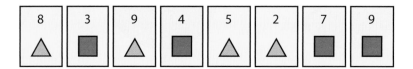

Joe mixes them up and puts them face down on the table.
Then he turns the first card over, like this:

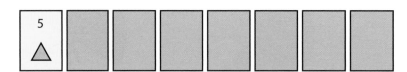

Joe is going to turn the next card over. Copy and complete this sentence:

On the next card, ……………… is less likely than ………………

d The number on the next card could be higher than 5 or lower than 5.
Which is more likely? Write the letter.

A   higher than 5   B   lower than 5   C   cannot tell

Explain your answer.

Points to remember

⊙ Probabilities are usually written as fractions or decimals but are sometimes written as percentages.

⊙ For equally likely outcomes, the **theoretical probability** of an event is:

$$\frac{\text{number of favourable outcomes}}{\text{total number of possible outcomes}}$$

⊙ The **experimental probability** of an event is:

$$\frac{\text{number of successful trials}}{\text{total number of trials}}$$

Revision unit 2

This unit will help you to:

- ⊙ revise the work you have done so far during the year;
- ⊙ answer test questions.

Many of the questions are from National Curriculum test papers (SATs).

1 Solving word problems

This lesson will remind you how to solve word problems.

To solve word problems:

- ⊙ read the problem and identify key information;
- ⊙ write down what calculation(s) you will do;
- ⊙ change units to the same unit if you need to;
- ⊙ decide whether to do the calculation mentally, using a written method or using a calculator;
- ⊙ record your answer, including any units;
- ⊙ check your answer carefully to make sure that it makes sense;
- ⊙ decide what else you need to write to explain your answer.

Exercise 1
Do questions 1–4 **without using a calculator**.

1. *2000 level 4*

   Mark and James have the same birthday.
   They were born on 15th March in different years.

   a Mark was 12 years old on 15th March 2001.
   How old will he be on 15th March 2020?

   b In what year was Mark born?

   c James was half of Mark's age on 15th March 2001.
   In what year was James born?

② *2002 level 4*

How much does it cost to park for 40 minutes?
Show your working.

P Car Park
Car Park Charges
15p for **8 minutes**

③ *2004 level 4*

I buy a widescreen television costing £1290.
I pay £900 now, then I pay the rest of the money in 3 equal payments.
How much is each payment?

④ *2001 level 5*

a A football club is planning a trip.
The club hires 234 coaches. Each coach holds 52 passengers.
How many passengers is that altogether?

b The club wants to put one first-aid kit into each of the 234 coaches.
These first-aid kits are sold in boxes of 18.
How many boxes does the club need?

You may **use your calculator** to work out the answer to question 5.
Remember to write down the calculation that you do.

⑤ *1996 level 5*

Bill, Ravi and Eric are three divers in a competition.

Each type of dive has a dive rating. Easy dives have a low rating; hard dives have a high rating.

Every dive is marked by five judges.
Each judge gives a mark out of 10.

This is how to calculate the score for a dive:

● Remove the highest and the lowest marks.

● Add together the middle three marks

● Multiply this total by the dive rating.

a Bill does a dive with a dive rating of 3.34.
The judges give the marks:

7.0   7.5   8.0   8.0   8.5

What is Bill's score?

b Ravi scored 82.68 on his first dive. The dive had a dive rating of 3.18.
What was the total of the middle three marks given by the judges?

c Eric is getting ready to take his final dive.
He needs to score at least 102.69 to win the competition.
Eric decides to do a dive with a dive rating of 3.26.
Explain why Eric has made a poor decision.

Points to remember

⊙ Read word problems carefully and identify key information.

⊙ Change units to the same unit if necessary.

⊙ Write down the calculation that you need to do.

⊙ Choose efficient calculation methods.

⊙ Show your working, including in calculator questions. You may get a mark for your method.

⊙ Write down your answer to the problem. Include any units.

⊙ Decide what to record to 'explain your answer'.

⊙ Look back at the original problem and check that the answer is sensible and about the right size.

2 Ratio

This lesson will remind you how to solve problems involving ratios.

Simplify ratios like fractions by dividing each side by the same number.

Example 1   Simplify the ratio 16:24.

Both 16 and 24 divide exactly by 8, so divide both sides by 8.
The ratio 16:24 is equivalent to 2:3.

To divide a quantity into two parts in the ratio $a:b$, begin by dividing the quantity into $a + b$ equal units. Put a units in one part, and b units in the other part.

Example 2   Divide 6 kg of carrots in the ratio 7:3.

You need 7 + 3 = 10 equal units.
For one unit, calculate 6 kg ÷ 10 = 0.6 kg.
For seven units, calculate 0.6 kg × 7 = 4.2 kg.
For three units, calculate 0.6 kg × 3 = 1.8 kg.

So 6 kg divided in the ratio 7:3 is 4.2 kg : 1.8 kg.

Given a ratio and the size of one part, you can find the other part.

Example 3

A line segment is divided into two parts in the ratio 2 : 3.
The shorter part of the line is 12 cm long.
What is the length of the longer part?

12 cm represents two equal units.
For one unit, calculate 12 cm ÷ 2 = 6 cm.
For three units, calculate 6 cm × 3 = 18 cm.

So the longer part of the line is 18 cm.

Exercise 2

Solve these problems **without using a calculator**. Show your working clearly.

1. A drink uses apple juice and orange juice in the ratio 2 : 3.
   I want to make 1 litre of this drink.
   How many millilitres of apple juice should I use?

2. At a cinema there are 900 seats.
   There are twice as many seats downstairs as upstairs.
   How many seats are downstairs?

3. In 1998 there were 135 000 people who
   were at least 100 years old.

   The ratio of males to females was 1 : 4.

   How many of them were females?

4. Jill and Michael's grandmother left them some money.
   They shared the money in the ratio 2 : 3.

   Jill's share was £110.

   How much was Michael's share?

5. *1998 level 5*

   To make purple paint you mix 3 parts red paint to 7 parts blue paint.
   Paul mixed 4.5 litres of red paint with some blue paint to make purple paint.
   How many litres of blue paint did he use?

6 *1999 level 5*

   a Nigel pours 1 carton of apple juice and 3 cartons of orange juice into a big jug.
      What is the ratio of apple juice to orange juice in Nigel's jug?

   b Lesley pours 1 carton of apple juice and $1\frac{1}{2}$ cartons of orange juice into another big jug.
      What is the ratio of apple juice to orange juice in Lesley's jug?

   c Tandi pours 1 carton of apple juice and 1 carton of orange juice into another big jug.
      She wants only half as much apple juice as orange juice in her jug.
      What should Tandi pour into her jug now?

7 *2002 level 5*

The number 6 is halfway between 4.5 and 7.5.

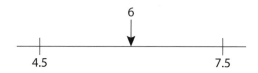

Copy and complete these sentences.

   a The number 6 is halfway between 2.8 and …

   b The number 6 is halfway between −12 and …

8 The distance from A to C is 80 cm.

The distance from A to B is four times as far as from B to C.
Calculate the distance from A to B.

Points to remember

⊙ To simplify a ratio, divide each side by the same number.
  For example, 5 : 10 is equivalent to 1 : 2.

⊙ To divide a quantity into two parts in the ratio 2 : 7, divide it into
  2 + 7 = 9 equal shares. Put 2 shares in one part, and 7 shares in the
  other part.

3 Sequences, functions and graphs

This lesson will remind you how to generate sequences and plot the graphs of simple functions.

You can work out the next number in a sequence if you know the **term-to-term rule.**

You can work out any term in a sequence if you know the formula for the n**th term.**

Example 1

Here is a sequence of patterns made up of crosses.

$$
\begin{array}{cccc}
\times & \times\ \times & \times\ \times\ \times & \times\ \times\ \times\ \times \\
\times & \times\ \times & \times\ \times\ \times & \times\ \times\ \times\ \times \\
\text{Pattern 1} & \text{Pattern 2} & \text{Pattern 3} & \text{Pattern 4}
\end{array}
$$

a Complete the table.

Pattern number	1	2	3	4	5	6
Number of crosses	2	4	6	8		

The rule for the sequence is 'add 2'.
The 5th term is $8 + 2 = 10$. The 6th term is $10 + 2 = 12$.

b Write a formula for the nth term of the sequence.

Each term in the sequence is double the pattern number.
The nth term of the sequence is $2 \times n = 2n$.

c Use the formula for the nth term to work out the 50th term of the sequence.

Substitute $n = 50$ in the formula $2n$.
The 50th term of the sequence is $2 \times 50 = 100$.

Graphs can show the relationship between two quantities.

Example 2

This graph shows the relationship between the number of litres of petrol and the total cost.

Use the graph to estimate:

a the cost of 18 litres of petrol;

For 18 litres of petrol the cost is £16.

b how much petrol you can buy for £40.

For £40, you can buy approximately 45 litres of petrol.

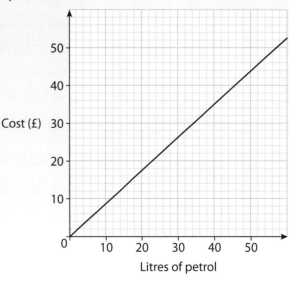

1 *Year 7 Optional Test level 4*

Here is part of a number sequence.

..., 7, 11, 19, 35, ...

To get the next number you multiply by 2 then subtract 3.

Copy the sequence. Fill in the two missing numbers.

2 *1998 level 4*

Owen has some tiles like these:

He uses the tiles to make a series of patterns.

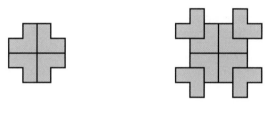

Pattern 1   Pattern 2

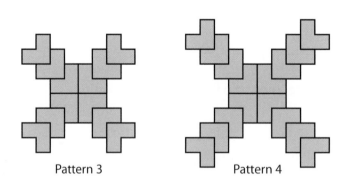

Pattern 3   Pattern 4

a   Each new pattern has more tiles than the one before.
The number of tiles goes up by the same amount each time.
How many more tiles does Owen add each time he makes a new pattern?

b   How many tiles will Owen need altogether to make pattern number 6?

c   How many tiles will Owen need altogether to make pattern number 9?

d   Owen uses 40 tiles to make a pattern.
What is the number of the pattern he makes?

You can make 'huts' with matches.

 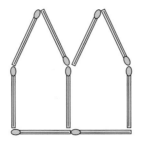 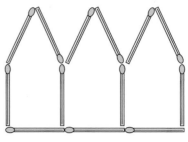

| 1 hut needs | 2 huts need | 3 huts need |
| 5 matches | 9 matches | 13 matches |

A rule to find how many matches you need is

$$m = 4h + 1$$

m stands for the number of matches.
h stands for the number of huts.

a Use the rule to find how many matches you need to make 8 huts.
Show your working.

b I use 81 matches to make some huts. How many huts do I make?
Show your working.

c Andy makes different 'huts' with matches.

 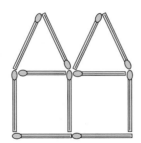 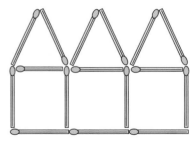

| 1 hut needs | 2 huts need | 3 huts need |
| 6 matches | 11 matches | 16 matches |

Which of the rules below shows how many matches he needs?

Remember: *m* stands for the number of matches.

              h stands for the number of huts.

$m = h + 5$ $m = 4h + 2$ $m = 4h + 3$

$m = 5h + 1$ $m = 5h + 2$ $m = h + 13$

4 *2002 KS2 level 4*

This graph shows the cost of phone
calls in the daytime and in the evening.

a Estimate how much it costs to
make a 9 minute call in the daytime.

b How much more does it cost to
make a 6 minute call in the daytime
than in the evening?

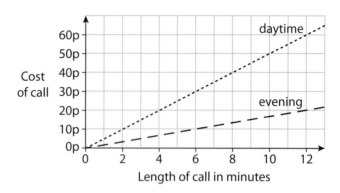

5 *1997 level 5*

The Highway Code states the minimum distance there should be between cars.
There are different distances for bad weather and good weather.
The graph below shows this.

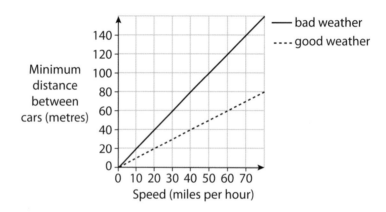

a The weather is bad.
   A car is travelling at 40 miles per hour.
   What is the minimum distance it should be from the car in front?

b The weather is good.
   A car is travelling at 55 miles per hour.
   What is the minimum distance it should be from the car in front?

c Mr Evans is driving 30 metres behind another car.
   The weather is bad.
   What is the maximum speed at which Mr Evans should be driving?

d Mrs Singh is driving at 50 miles per hour in good weather.
   She is the minimum distance from the car in front.
   It begins to rain heavily. Both cars slow down to 30 miles per hour.
   Use the graph to work out how much Mrs Singh must increase her distance
   from the car in front.
   Show your working.

Points to remember

- A sequence of numbers follows a rule.
- You can work out the next term in a sequence if you know the term-to-term rule.
- You can work out any term in a sequence if you know the formula for the nth term.
- A coordinate point is represented by an ordered pair of numbers (x, y).
- Always inspect the labels and axes on a graph before reading any values.
- Take care when reading the scales on the axes of graphs. Work out the value of intervals carefully.

4 Area and perimeter

This lesson will remind you how to solve problems involving area and perimeter.

Perimeter is the distance all the way round the edge of a 2D shape.

The units of perimeter are the units of length, so it can be measured in millimetres (mm), centimetres (cm), metres (m) or kilometres (km), for example.

Example 1

What is the perimeter of this shape?
All the corners are right angles.

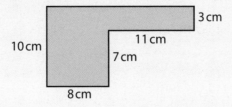

The length of one of the six sides is not given in the diagram. Work out the length of this side first.

Missing length = 8 cm + 11 cm = 19 cm

Perimeter = 19 + 3 + 11 + 7 + 8 + 10 = 58 cm

The **area** of a two-dimensional shape is a measure of the amount of space covered by the shape.

Area is measured in square millimetres (mm²), square centimetres (cm²), square metres or square kilometres (km²).

To find the **area of a rectangle**, multiply its length by its width.

Example 2

Work out the area of the rectangle.

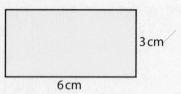

Area of rectangle = length × width = 6 × 3 = 18 cm²

Example 3

This shape is drawn on a centimetre square grid.
Estimate its area.

Count each part of a square which is a half a square or more as a whole square. Ignore each part of a square which is less than half a square.

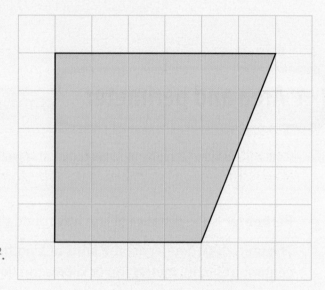

Number of whole squares 22
Total of part squares 3 whole squares
The area of the shape is about 22 + 3 = 25 cm².

Example 4

A piece of card is in the shape of a rectangle.
A rectangular hole is cut from the card as shown.
The hole is 4 cm by 2 cm.

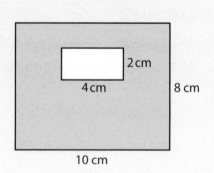

What is the area of the card that is left?

To find the area of card that is left, take the area of the hole away from the area of the large rectangle.

Area of large rectangle = 10 × 8 = 80 cm²

Area of hole = 4 × 2 = 8 cm²

Area of card left = (80 − 8) cm² = 72 cm²

Example 5

What is the surface area of a cube of edge 2 cm?

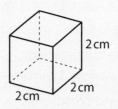

The net of the cube shows its six square faces.

The area of each square face is $2 \times 2 = 4\,cm^2$.
So the surface area of the cube is $6 \times 4 = 24\,cm^2$.

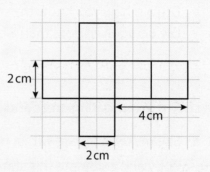

Exercise 4

You will need centimetre squared paper.

(1) *2005 level 4*

Look at the diagram on each centimetre square grid.
Work out the area that is shaded on each diagram.

a

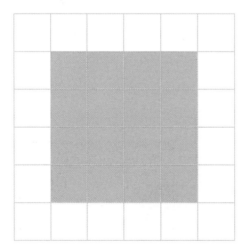

b

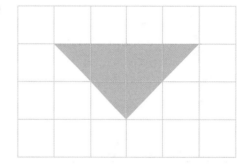

c

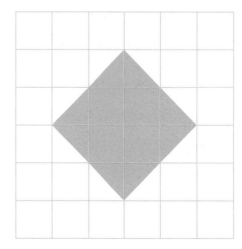

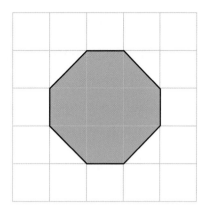

2 *2000 level 4*

  a Look at the octagon.

    It is drawn on a centimetre square grid.

    Copy and complete this sentence.

    The area of the octagon is … cm².

  b Explain how you know that the perimeter of
the octagon is more than 8 cm.

3 *1996 level 5*

Lucy is investigating areas and perimeters of shapes.

  a She makes a square with a perimeter of 24 cm.

    Copy and complete this statement:

    Area of square = … cm²

NOT TO SCALE

  b Lucy makes a rectangle with a perimeter of 24 cm.
The length is twice the width.

    Calculate the area of her rectangle.
Copy and complete this statement:

    Area of rectangle = … cm²

NOT TO SCALE

4 *2004 level 4*

Here is a shaded shape on a centimetre square grid.

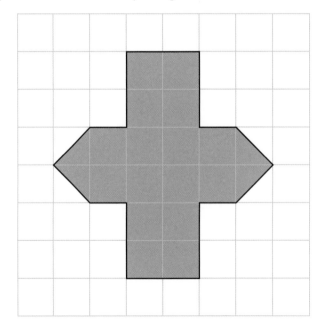

  a What is the area of the shaded shape?

  b On centimetre squared paper draw a rectangle that has the same area as the shaded shape.

The diagram shows a box.

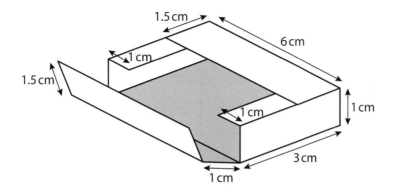

In the centre of an A4 piece of centimetre squared paper, copy the rectangle below. Complete the net for the box.

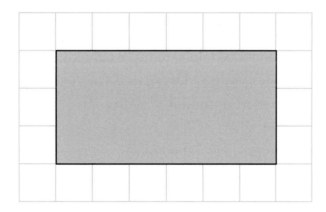

1995 level 5

Some of these nets can be folded to make cuboids.

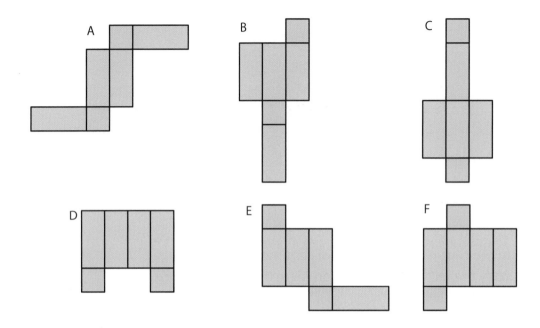

a Which nets can be folded to make cuboids?

b Choose two nets which cannot be folded to make cuboids.

   Explain why one of the nets cannot be folded to make a cuboid.
   You can write your explanation, or show it on a diagram.
   Say which net you have chosen.

c Explain why the other net cannot be folded to make a cuboid.
   You can write your explanation, or show it on a diagram.
   Say which net you have chosen.

Points to remember

⊙ **Perimeter** is the distance around the edge of a shape.

⊙ **Area** is a measure of the surface covered by a shape.

⊙ Area of a rectangle = length × width.

⊙ To find the surface area of a 3D shape, add the areas of all its faces.

⊙ A **net** is a 2D surface that can be folded into a 3D shape or solid.

5 Symmetry and transformations

This lesson will remind you how to identify transformations and symmetries of 2D shapes.

In a **translation**:

- all points of the shape move the same distance in the same direction;
- the angles of the shape and the lengths of the sides stay the same;
- the shape does not turn.

To describe a **translation** you must describe:

- the horizontal distance that the shape moves;
- the vertical distance that the shape moves.

Shape A has been translated 3 squares to the right and 5 squares up.

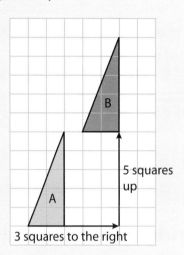

In a **reflection**:

- the angles of the shape and the lengths of the sides stay the same;
- the shape is flipped;
- the reflection is as far behind the mirror line as the shape is in front.

To describe a **reflection** you must give:

- the mirror line.

Triangle B is the reflection of triangle A in the mirror line. Also, triangle A is the reflection of triangle B in the mirror line. (Mirror lines are like two-way mirrors.)

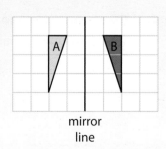

In a **rotation**:

- ● the angles of the shape and the lengths of the sides stay the same;
- ● the shape turns;
- ● the centre of rotation does not move.

To describe a **rotation** you must give:

- ● the angle of turn;
- ● the direction of turn, clockwise or anticlockwise;
- ● the point the shape turns about (the **centre of rotation**).

Shape A has been rotated 90° clockwise about point O.

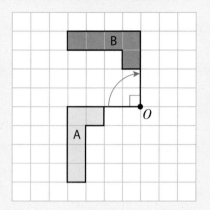

Exercise 5

① *2002 level 4*

    a I have a rectangle made out of paper. The rectangle measures 12 cm by 8 cm.

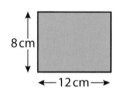

I want to fold the rectangle in half to make a smaller rectangle.
I can do this in two different ways.
What size could the smaller rectangle be?
Write both ways by copying and completing these:

first way: … cm by … cm

second way: … cm by … cm

    b I have a square made out of paper. The square measures 20 cm by 20 cm.
I keep folding it in half until I have a rectangle that is 5 cm by 10 cm.

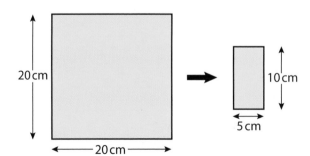

How many times did I fold it?

a I start with a rectangle of paper. I fold it in half, then I cut out three shapes.

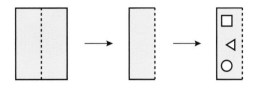

Then I unfold my paper. Write down the letter of the diagram below that shows what my paper looks like now.

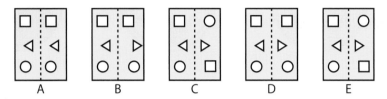

b I start again with a different rectangle of paper. I fold it in half, then in half again, then I cut out two shapes.

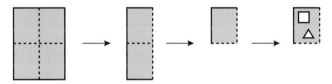

Then I unfold my paper. Write down the letter of the diagram below that shows what my paper looks like now.

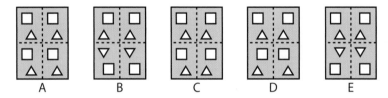

c I start with a square of paper. I fold it in half, then in half again, then I cut out one shape.

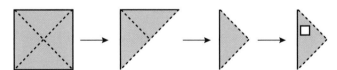

Then I unfold my paper. Write down the letter of the diagram below that shows what my paper looks like now.

3 *1995 level 4*

These patterns come from Egypt.
This first pattern looks the same after part of a turn.
It will look the same in 4 different positions.

In how many positions will each of these patterns look the same?
Write the number for each pattern.

a 　　b 　　c 　　d

4 *1999 level 5*

An equilateral triangle has
3 lines of symmetry.

It has rotation symmetry
of order 3.

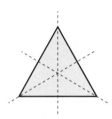　　　　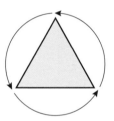

Look at each of these shapes.

Copy and complete the table. Write the letter of each shape in the correct space.

		Number of lines of symmetry			
		0	1	2	3
Order of rotation symmetry	1				
	2				
	3				

5 *Level 4*

a   What are the coordinates of point B?

b   The blue shape is reflected in a mirror line.
Point A stays in the same place.

Where is point B reflected to?
Write the coordinates.

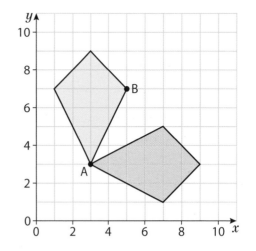

c   Now the blue shape is rotated about point A.

Where is point B rotated to?
Write the coordinates.

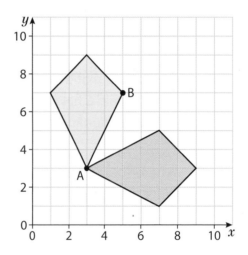

6   *2001 level 5*

Piece A of a card is shaded grey on the front,
and black on the back.

I turn piece A over to see its black side.

Which of the shapes below shows the black side
of piece A?

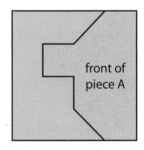

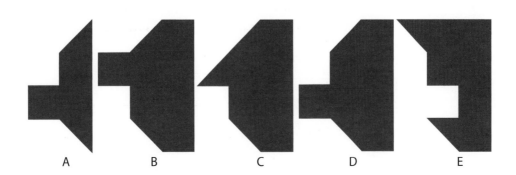

A   B   C   D   E

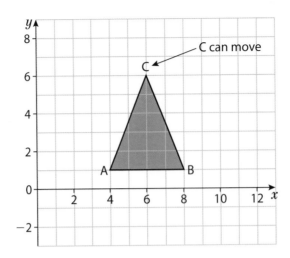

When C is at (6, 6), triangle ABC is isosceles.

a   C moves so that triangle ABC is still isosceles, with AB = BC.
Where could C have moved to?
Write the coordinates of its new position.

b   Then C moves so that triangle ABC is isosceles and right-angled.
Where could C have moved to?
Write the coordinates of its new position.

Points to remember

⊙ In a **reflection**, **rotation** or **translation**, the original shape (the object)
and the image are the same size and shape.

⊙ In a **translation**, each point of the object moves the same distance in
the same direction.

⊙ In a **reflection**, matching points of the object and image are the same
distance from the mirror line.

⊙ In a **rotation**, each point of the object turns about the centre of rotation
through the same angle in the same direction.

Answers to
How well are you doing?

N3.1

1 −4°C

2 −8

3 −10

4 7

5 −3

6 a 17　　　　　　　b 99

7 17 + 4 − (8 + 6) = 7

8 5 and 7 are both factors of 35

9 Any of 102, 105, …

10 24

A3.1

1 3, **7**, **11**, **15**, 19

2 a **20** → 40 → 80 → 160 → **320**

  b 40 → 20 → 10 → **5** → **2.5**

3 a $n = 3$　　　　b $m = 10$

4 17 cm

5 a 60 white tiles　　b 32 blue tiles

N3.2

1 100

2 a 367　　　　　b 0.580 (or 0.58)

3 Many possible answers e.g. 3.5.

4 0.071, 0.107, 0.17, 0.71

5 a 56 300　　　　b 5.1

6 0.8

7 10 × 14 = 140

8 a 48.22　　　　b 20 748

9 a 58.17　　　　b 520.608

10 a **13** × 59 = 767　　b **14** × **29** = **406**

G3.1

1 12 square units

2 a 40 cm　　　　b 72 cm²

3 52 cm²

4 10 cubes

5

N3.3

1 210

2 $\frac{4}{5}$

3 $\frac{1}{3}$

4 37%, 0.34

5 £180

6 80%

7 10 minutes

8 12 pupils; 50%

9 $\frac{1}{12}$

S3.1

1 a Monday and Thursday　b 8 pupils

2 a 1 day　　　　　　b 5–9 bottles

3 a 55%　　　　　　b 5 pupils

4 a Claire　　　　　b Claire, Tom

5 a Any two ages with a difference of seven
　　e.g. 9 and 2.

  b 0

G3.2

1 a Acute

  b No; they are the same size.

2 a 45°　　　　　　b 115°

3 Pupils' own accurate constructions.

4 No; 24 + 93 + 61 = 178 and angles on a straight
line add up to 180°.

5 a 113° angles on a straight line total 180°
 b 71° angles on a straight line total 180°
 c 90° angles on a straight line total 180°
 d 37° opposite angles are equal
 e 60° angles at a point total 360°
 f 72° angles at a point total 360°

S3.2

1 a True; both outcomes equally likely.
 b False; probabilities are theoretical, in practice outcomes may be different.
2 a $\frac{1}{4}$ b 10 red counters
3 E
4 a $\frac{1}{20}$ b green
5 a $\frac{1}{35}$ b $\frac{16}{35}$

N3.4

1 a 12 000 g   b 1500 m
 c 2500 ml   d 100 mm²

2

	grams	kilograms
potatoes	3500	3.5
apples	1200	1.2
grapes	250	0.25
ginger	30	0.03
carrots	600	0.6

3 a A   b C   c C
4 a 42   b 12 216
5 a 6h 14m   b 25p
6 a 8.7 cm   b 1.4 m
7 a 850 ml   b 24 days
8 a **60 × 50 = 3**000   b **134 × 5 = 670**

A3.2

1 a £200   b 14 days
2 a Any correct pair that sum to 30 e.g. 1 + 29.
 b $b = 10$
3 a $8k + 7$ b $2k + 5$
4 a $8p + 12$ b $15p + 21$
5 a 23   b 20   c 33
6 a $k = 4$ b $t = -7$

S3.3

1 a There is no box to tick if you are **exactly** 18 years old.
 b 18 years old or over.
2 a

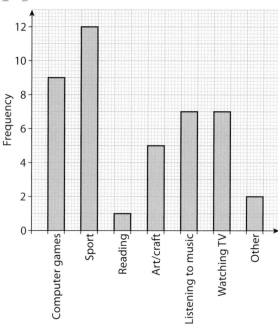

Favourite hobby

 b Any valid conclusion, e.g the same number liked listening to music and watching television.
3 a September
 b May, June, October, November, December
 c December, January, February
4 a $\frac{1}{8}$ b 40

A3.3

1 a A (0, 6); C (4, 3)   b D (2, 7)
2 a $y = 4$ b $x = -1$
 c $x = 3$ d $y = -2$
3

x	-2	-1	0	1	2	3
$y = 3x + 2$	-4	-1	2	5	8	11

4 **a** e.g. (0, 5) (1, 6) (2, 4) etc

b

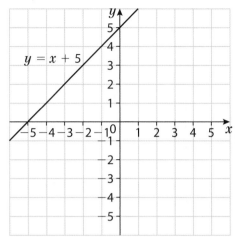

5 −1, 2, 5, 8, 11

6 **a** 49, 64, 81   **b** n^2

G3.3

1

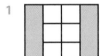

2 D

3

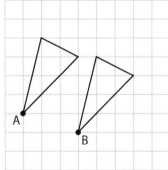

4

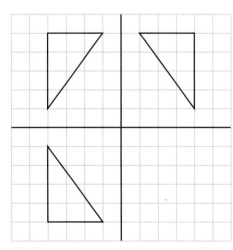

5

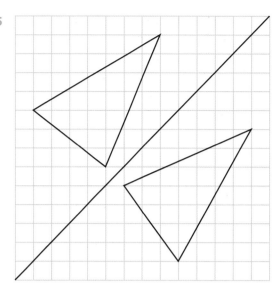

N3.5

1 **a** 60%

   b 60 pupils

   c 100 pupils → 5 teachers

   106 pupils → 6 teachers

   197 pupils → 10 teachers

2 **a** 200 g   **b** 8   **c** 2:3

3 **a** 1:3   **b** 2:3

   c One more carton of orange juice.

4 **a** 6 litres of red and 14 litres of blue.

   b 6 litres of yellow and 4 litres of red.

5 24 minutes

6 30 eggs

G3.4

1 **a** True   **b** False

   c False   **d** True

2 No. A rectangle also has four right-angles.

3 **a** 60°, 60°, 60°   **b** 90°, 45°, 45°

4 (3, 0) (4, 1) (5, 2) (6, 3) (4, 3) (6, 1) (7, 0)

5 $a = 65°, b = 155°$

6 Any correct quadrilateral with only two right-angles (kite or trapezium).

S3.4

1 **a** They are unlikely to get truthful responses.

   b They are recording data in only one place and at one time of the day/week.

2 Hannah's mean daily distance is
$(32.3 + 38.7 + 43.5 + 45.1) \div 4 = 39.9$ km, which
is less than 40 km.

3 a Size 6   **b** Size 2

4 a Year 10

   b Magazines

   c e.g. Year 10 spent more on CDs and clothes.
Year 7 spent more on sweets and savings.

G3.5

1 270°

2 a Q

   b Pupils' own accurate constructions of 157°
angles.

3 Pupils' own accurate constructions.

4 C and D

5 A, B and D

6

A3.4

1 a D   **b** $8b + 3$

2 a $y = 18$ **b** $y = 2$ **c** C

3 a $x = 14$ **b** $y = 13$

4 61

5 a £30.00

   b Between four and five years old.

S3.5

1 a Any five numbers all less than 6.

   b 3 even and 2 odd numbers OR 4 even and 1
odd number.

   c Any five numbers that are **not** multiples of 3.

2 a 2 correct outcomes from 4 coins so
probability $= \frac{2}{4} = \frac{1}{2}$.

   b 4 coins totalling 33p are 20p, 10, 2p, 1p, so
probability of 10p $= \frac{1}{4}$.

3 a The probability that the flavour will be **plain** is $\frac{1}{2}$.
The probability that the flavour will be cheese
is $\frac{1}{10}$.

   b $\frac{1}{8}$

   c Plain 7, vinegar 3, chicken 2, cheese 0.

N3.6

1 30

2 12.86

3 £4.57

4 a £33.25   **b** 14 trees

5 a $\frac{2}{12} = \frac{1}{6}$ **b** $\frac{1}{2} = \frac{12}{24}$ **c** $\frac{3}{12} = \frac{6}{24}$

6 a $\frac{3}{4}$ of 100 $= \frac{1}{2}$ of **150**

   b $\frac{1}{3}$ of 60 $= \frac{2}{3}$ of **30**

   c $\frac{3}{8} + \frac{1}{3} = \frac{17}{24}$

   d $\frac{5}{6} - \frac{1}{3} = \frac{1}{2}$

7 a 600 ml

   b 50 ml

   c No. $\frac{1}{5} = 20\%$ of the mixture is screenwash.

8 a $\frac{1}{3}$

   b $\frac{2}{5}$

   c Shape A has $\frac{1}{4}$ shaded, shape B has $\frac{3}{13}$ shaded,
which is less than $\frac{1}{4}$.

9 a £2.12   **b** £12.25

Index